MW01038600

Advance Praise for
The Art of Medical Leadership

Major change is afoot in healthcare. Effective leadership at all levels is critical. In this book, the authors present an excellent roadmap for any member of the healthcare team in a practice to learn and enhance their leadership skills. The concepts and skill sets are provided in a straightforward and powerful way for the reader. Each chapter is loaded with high-level as well as practical material and concludes with a set of "to do" items for real learning and acting. I strongly recommend this book for anyone working in a medical practice interested in enhancing their ability to lead themselves, their teams, and their enterprise.

Len Fromer, MD, FAAFP
Executive Medical Director
Group Practice Forum

In *The Art of Medical Leadership*, Suzan and Scott have provided a blueprint for transforming a medical office into a mission/vision-driven, high-performing team.

I know from experience that the information is powerful when effectively applied, having been part of a company that had the wisdom to hire Suzan Oran as a consultant in 1989. Through effective implementation of the knowledge contained in this book, we became a high-performing company where people loved to work. We contracted with hospitals to run their emergency departments. We grew from four contracts in one city to twenty-two contracts in seven states before we sold to a national contract management group.

You will get a new sense of what is possible for your practice by reading this book. My personal opinion is that you will want Suzan, or someone she recommends, to accelerate transforming your practice using these principles.

David Pillow, MD
Medical Director, Emergency Department
William P. Clements Jr. University Hospital, Dallas, Texas
Past President, Texas College of Emergency Physicians

A must read for any physician looking to be successful in practice, provide true patient-centered care, and be of value in their community. This book provides a clear path to an efficient and effective practice by recognizing and reconciling the role of the physician as the practice leader and the staff as engaged team members.

Such a highly developed team, led by the physician, is well suited to focus on and address the needs of patients in a well-coordinated fashion. Such a highly developed team, led by the physician, is well suited to deliver on the promise of the Triple Aim—improved patient health status, reduced healthcare spending, and high levels of satisfaction with care delivery and outcomes.

Jed Constantz, CEO
Employer Advantage Health Care Solutions

This book defines a "how to" leadership roadmap to change a medical practice culture from the traditional service provider model to a high-performance team with a mission to improve the patient experience, employee satisfaction, and practice efficiency. This is a must read for healthcare leaders!

John P. Strapp Jr.
Cofounder and Chairman
The Kinetix Group

The Art of Medical Leadership is a unique combination of sound leadership and experience that is a must read for physicians as well as non-physicians that plan to become the next generation of medical leaders. As pointed out by the authors, the skills of becoming an effective leader are quite different from the skills of practicing medicine. Suzan Oran and Scott Conard come from very different professional backgrounds and points of view that, when mixed together, form an excellent blend of experiences, passion, and vision necessary to become a great leader.

Patrick Dunn, MS/MBA
Your Heart Score

The Art of Medical Leadership contains pearls with practical impact. For those ready to move beyond the typically informal leadership skills gained during medical training, Scott and Suzan redefine listening, team building, and motivating in a whole new way. I recommend *The Art of Medical Leadership* for colleagues looking to take their practice and patient care to the next level.

Alyssa McManamon, MD
Hematologist–Oncologist

Suzan Oran and Dr. Scott Conard provide practical techniques to help leaders more effectively manage teams, engage others, and cast vision. An excellent leadership must read for healthcare professionals.

Robert L. Duhaney, MD
Internal Medicine of Addison
Texas Health Physicians Group

The Art of Medical Leadership is fantastic, just the right blend of theory and practical application. It is a must-read guide for medical leaders interested in learning the path toward transforming themselves and their organizations. Bravo!

Tracy Duberman, PhD
President and CEO
The Leadership Development Group, Inc.

The *Art* of
MEDICAL
LEADERSHIP

The *Art* of MEDICAL LEADERSHIP

Expand Your Influence

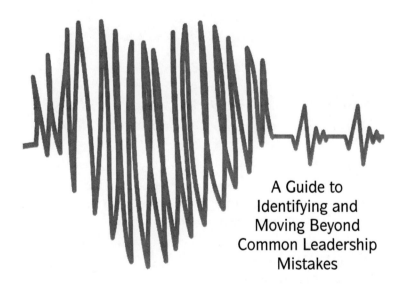

A Guide to
Identifying and
Moving Beyond
Common Leadership
Mistakes

SUZAN ORAN AND SCOTT CONARD, MD
with Nicole Oran

The Art of Medical Leadership: Expand Your Influence; A Guide to Identifying and Moving Beyond Common Leadership Mistakes

Copyright © 2015 Suzan Oran, Scott Conard, and Nicole Oran. All rights reserved. No part of this book may be reproduced or retransmitted in any form or by any means without the written permission of the publisher.

Published by Wheatmark®
1760 East River Road, Suite 145
Tucson, Arizona 85718 USA
www.wheatmark.com

ISBN: 978-1-62787-177-8 (paperback)
ISBN: 978-1-62787-178-5 (ebook)
LCCN: 2014955438

Contents

Foreword

By Lynn Myers, MD

Accountable care requires that we work together. *All* of us working at the top of our licenses, certifications, and qualifications. And accountable care starts with *accountable leadership*—leadership at all levels in a practice.

In this book, Suzan and Scott tell the story of effective, authentic communication and an intentional way of being that allows us to be accountable in our professional role as medical leaders, helps us learn how to build teams and gain consensus, and gives practical guidance that, with practice, leads to confidence in this new identity.

What can I say? As a doctor and the captain of my practice, I had the last word in every conversation and I was usually the smartest person in the room. *Oh boy*—while that might have worked for a while in the narrow arena of the doctor-patient relationship, it did not work at all when I transitioned to the corporate side of medicine. Truth be known, it probably didn't work that well in my practice either, where building consensus meant that I decided what would be done and you agreed with me. Sound familiar?

The distinctions presented in this book of being a *learner* (instead of a *knower*) had not been part of my lexicon since my days as a med student and resident. Taking me out of the clinic and putting me in the C-suite of a successful physician management group meant that I would need to work on a team, learn to delegate tasks, inspire action, and embrace change. Suzan and Scott have provided a different perspective and a collection of tools that you can apply to do just that, no matter what role you have in a medical organization.

As physicians in leadership, we naturally are hired in director (and higher) roles and are chosen to lead or colead committees, teams, and departments. But medical school does not equip us with the corporate language or teach us to navigate the infrastructure of complex organizations. Physician leaders must make the leap from being "The Doctor" to a member of the larger team. For some of us it can take a while to get comfortable with earning respect in this environment without the mantle of the stethoscope and lab coat that provides instant credibility.

This book provides a different way of approaching what you want to accomplish in your medical practice. It can help everyone on the team rise to a new level in their endeavor for a successful practice and, most importantly, the best care possible for patients.

Lynn Myers, MD
Medical Director of Quality
Coding and Medical Education
Texas Health Physicians Group

Preface

How to Use This Book

In these changing times in healthcare it takes a lot just to keep up, let alone get ahead.

We respect your time and know that you are very busy implementing new policies and procedures while taking good care of your patients!

Our commitment is to provide a useful and inspiring collection of information that you can use to:

- Increase your effectiveness and success in your role with medicine

- Increase collaboration, teamwork, and creative problem solving by you and your team so that your patients receive the very best care possible and everyone on the team experiences deeper satisfaction with their job

Although we have written this book with a medical practice in mind, the information is equally applicable and effective in a clinic, hospital department, emergency room, or any group focused on caring for patients.

You can learn from this book by:

- Starting at the beginning and reading each chapter in sequence, not moving to the next chapter until you are fully utilizing what was covered in that chapter

or

- Reading it cover to cover first, then going back to chapter one and taking a week or more per chapter to intentionally apply the distinctions and suggestions

or

- Glancing through the book and selecting a chapter that covers a topic that you're interested in, then actively applying it

or

- Glancing through, picking up bits and pieces that resonate for you, and applying those

You can use this book to make a small, medium, or large difference in your practice—we truly respect whatever is right for you!

Acknowledgments

It is a privilege for me to share the information in this book! This is a collection of distinctions, ideas, and processes that I have learned from many teachers, gained from the gift of working with my clients since 1986 as well as discovered from my personal life experiences. I could never list everyone that has in some way had a role in what I'm expressing in this book. That said, I will take the opportunity to acknowledge a few.

I acknowledge first my husband, Haluk Oran. We met in 1981, married in 1982, and have been using all of the relationship distinctions in this book throughout our marriage. He is my best friend, and it is a profound gift for me to live my life with him! He supports me in everything I do, including the process of writing this book. He spent significant time reviewing, making suggestions, and helping us fine-tune the final manuscript. He has a deep grasp of these distinctions and is skilled in increasing their clarity when presenting them to others.

I acknowledge Nicole Oran, my daughter. I am so thankful for our unique and very special relationship. Her creativity and clever sense of humor is a gift. She has provided hands-on support for the writing process of this book as well as background support. Her creative writing voice helped me find mine. I credit her with empowering me to have the courage to take on this project!

I acknowledge Paul Oran, my son. I am deeply thankful for our dynamic relationship. Paul is a scientist and entrepreneur with a spark for creating what doesn't yet exist. He fosters our family commitment to play full out and to be expressed in life!

I acknowledge my father, Paul Almquist. He has been the primary stabilizing force throughout my life with his deep appreciation of and commitment to effective communication. He has been a role model with his view that anything is possible and that the world is our playground. He has an open heart and love for me. I am deeply grateful for our relationship and his loving influence on our family!

I acknowledge my mother, Bettie Almquist. During her short life of forty-one years, she contributed to me greatly. She taught me to be open-minded toward other people's points of view, to appreciate our differences, and to realize that it is a privilege to do volunteer work to support others.

Also, I acknowledge all of my family and friends for adding a wonderful, rich depth to my life!

I honor Werner Erhard for his influence on my work and in my life. I had the privilege of working with and being trained to lead seminars by the staff at Werner Erhard and Associates. I was first introduced to many of the distinctions and concepts in this book through Werner Erhard's body of work. A few of the people at WE&A who put their hearts and souls into training me to give my very best were David Zelman, Suzanne Bush Black, and Joan Garbo. Thank you!

My consulting and coaching work and all that is expressed in this book continues to evolve through my own experiences, what I learn from my clients, and the wisdom of other teachers, such as Louise Hay, Deepak Chopra, and Eckhart Tolle, just to name a few.

I acknowledge all of my clients for their contributions to me. I could never list everyone who has made a deep contribution to and impact on my life. A few of my clients (who are now friends) have had an extraordinary influence on me as well as my business through their taking a stand for what I have to offer, their openness to being coached, and their commitment to evolving in their own lives, as well as through the business opportunities they have fostered. A few people that stand out for me in that category are Lew Pincus, DO, (we miss you Lew!) and his wife, Ellen; David Pillow, MD, and his wife, Sunny; Ron Hellstern, MD; John Kruger, Mark Stout, Clay Heighten, MD, and his wife, Debra Caudy, MD; and Carl Soderstrom and his wife, Jennifer Lee.

I am forever grateful for the opportunity that Dr. Clay Heighten and Carl Soderstrom gave me to be the vice president of leadership development for Medical Edge Healthcare Group, PA. They went out of their way and beyond "standard business" to give everyone that was a part of Medical Edge and PhyServe Physician Services the opportunity to participate in my workshops and seminars, with a commitment to empowering them not only in their work but also in their personal lives. It was a deep privilege for me to work with all of the amazing people at Medical Edge who were so committed to making a difference through their work. They will always have a special place in my heart.

And finally, I acknowledge my coauthor, Dr. Scott

Conard. I am deeply inspired by his commitment to make a difference in healthcare and continue the never-ending opportunity to evolve in his personal self-expression. He is one of the amazing people I met and got to work with at Medical Edge. I am so thankful that he called me in January 2013 and asked if I was ready to put some of the content of my consulting and workshops into a book with him. I said yes, and we were off and running!

Suzan

Acknowledgments

There were times, as I learned and deployed the concepts in this book, that it felt uncomfortable, unnatural, and very different from my opinion on how to run an office or a company. It was the confidence of Dr. Clay Heighten and Carl Soderstrom in these distinctions and the teaching methods of Suzan Oran that kept me focused and convinced it would work.

Suzan Oran's lifelong commitment to mastering and perfecting her art, coupled with her positivity, enthusiasm, and unfaltering confidence in those she teaches, creates an inspiring and effective crucible for learning. It was Clay and Carl's belief that the truth and utility of these concepts would empower the medical group of more than 3,600 employees to be one in which the employees themselves initiated and led innovation and improvement.

In the end, the top few leaders can make the concepts and information available, but the operational leaders must learn, embrace, teach, coach, and manage transformation. Lori Clay, Jennifer Lee, Cora Bennett, and David Moye encouraged and supported the directors of operations like

Katie Bozell, Faith Harty, Steve Wilson, Dreux Bourque, Andy Boedeker, Suzie Mailloux, Jacquie Tucker, Barbra Milwood, Allice Bellomy, Josh Daniel, Joe Holcomb, Kelly Holler, Chris Simdon, Wanda Obono, Ashley Anson, Mary McNeil, Joe Acosta, and Gina Seay, who in turn supported the day-to-day implementation of these distinctions. While they worked in the offices, key leaders like Lynn Myers, MD, Tim Wilson, Jonathan Cooper, Jeff Smith, Lisa Oleson, Darwin Goodspeed, and Jim Rogers embraced these concepts and inculcated them throughout the corporate offices.

Three outstanding physician leaders led the charge and supported continual growth and improvement. Doctors Donald Fowler, Shawn Parsley, and Don Holt managed over one hundred doctors each in their respective regions. It was their vision and commitment to continually improve opportunities for the doctors that led to the incorporation of and participation in many in the programs Suzan and I taught. Their area leaders—Roger Tolar, Shehetaj Abdurrahim, Odilon Alvarado, Paul Anthony, John Arthur, Terrence Feehery, Eric Futscher, Alfred Hulse, Timothy McGuire, Carlos Mijares, Randall Perkins, Bane Smith, Ray Westbrook, John Wood, and Jack Wright—all deserve great credit for their vision and leadership.

I would like to thank Rand Stagen and the Stagen Institute, and in particular Rick Voirin, who provide ongoing cutting-edge leadership that supplements and complements the work in this book. Their Introduction to Leadership Program (ILP) and Graduate Leadership Program (GLP) are a continual source of inspiration and motivation for me, particularly the GLPx group—Doug Levy, Rick Sapio, Mitch Gervis, Tommy Glen, Rugger Burke,

Ken Adams, and Luke Sweetser—whose weekly cultivation of the pioneering spirit inspires ongoing confidence and determination.

I dedicate my work in this book to my daughter, Blair, who is currently in medical school. I am so proud to be her father. I hope that she has the opportunity to work alongside great leaders like Suzan and those acknowledged above to create and enjoy the empowered role of a physician in the new model of medicine.

Finally, I thank my partner for the last twenty-plus years, my wife, Susan, for her unfaltering support and love, and my sons, Nick, Alec, and Reed, for their belief in me and my work.

Scott

Introduction

Being part of a high-performance team in a medical office is a thrill. Having mutual respect and trust, as well as confidence in the skills and reliability of every teammate, allows each member to focus and perform at the highest possible level. Challenges are identified and solved, focused activity is high, and drama is low. Both the employees and the community the office serves experience a sense of accomplishment. Team members, from the least-trained employee to the lead doctor, feel they're contributing to an important cause and serving a vital role.

Does this sound like your office? If not, what would working in an office that operated this way do for your quality of life and for the quality of care the office provides?

As a leader, do you feel you have the skills to create this level of performance?

What if you could create and participate in this type of practice?

If you had told me this was possible in 2004 or 2005, I would have thought you a Pollyanna. At that point, I had practiced medicine for sixteen years, starting as a solo family practitioner in 1989 and growing my practice to twelve providers in three locations by 2005. In addition the practice had developed five sleep labs, a clinical research company, a durable medical equipment company, and a corporate wellness program company, as well as the management company. During this period, I served as founder, leader, doctor, and financial manager. The managers of each company, along with a group of shared human resources, legal, bookkeeping, and information technology staff, performed the daily operations. We had grown through internal funding and bootstrapping our efforts, so our leadership team was very lean and, in retrospect, more than a little overworked. At that point, I believed our team had achieved tremendous success compared to other groups, yet we had the sense that there were limits to what we could accomplish.

Frankly, we had sought but had not been able to achieve the elusive higher level of performance. We had done all we knew to do, from hiring process-oriented consultants to going to medical seminars, and yet we were achieving only incremental improvement. We were only looking for external answers, not realizing the real problem wouldn't be solved with new technology, another seminar, or a new hire to fill a hole in the workload. We later learned that breakthroughs come from gaining clarity and having distinctions in how we see situations.

When we have distinctions regarding how we are relating to ourselves and others as well as to our practices, we can choose a different path rather than following our automatic tendencies. As an example, to people who have not been trained to read an X-ray image, the screen looks like a bunch of blobs. But being trained to read X-rays provides distinctions that allow people to distinguish the different densities by color, from black to white. The X-ray image can now be useful. The problem in my practice was that my leadership team and I did not have the distinctions to transform our practice from a highly managed, autocratic, doctor-oriented system to a collaborative, conscious medical practice.

Then in 2006, I joined Medical Edge Healthcare Group and met Suzan Oran. Medical Edge was a medical management company that had 343 providers spanning North Carolina and Texas and was soon to expand to Nevada. It had grown over the past twelve years from a start-up to a rapidly growing and very successful enterprise. The team that managed this group had an extraordinary level of communication and collaboration. I must admit that it was not easy for me to fit into this model. I thought the best way I could contribute was to just make things happen. Gradually I began to see that true leadership was less about directing others and more about working well with them and fostering their full contribution. Frankly, I am still learning this way of operating. (It has been said that we are all "works in progress.") I do know that when I apply the distinctions in this book, the results are amazing; and when I revert back to old patterns, the cost is high.

The Medical Edge leadership team, headed by Dr. Clay Heighten and Carl Soderstrom, were committed to using a set of distinctions, some of which you will be introduced to in this book. They focused on continuing to improve and to involve people from every department, not only to keep up with the changes in healthcare but also to focus always on patient care. The guiding question was, "What's consis-

tent with our mission/vision statement?" People throughout operations, billing, IT, HR, and so on, were all pulling
together, keeping the patient ultimately in mind.

Initially I was skeptical, but over the next four years my
perspective completely changed. I gained an appreciation
for what was possible, and not only did it exceed my expectations, at times it seemed miraculous.

During my skeptical phase, I began to collect data and
document changes. The numbers confirmed undeniable
improvement as other practices joined Medical Edge, went
through a period of change lasting from nine to eighteen
months, and transformed to a different level and way of
providing care.

Three things consistently occurred:

1. The satisfaction of the employees, including the
   doctors, went up significantly.

2. The quality of care and service improved gradually and regularly.

3. The practice became much more successful financially and operationally.

There were many reasons for this success: better management and financial systems, stable personnel in the top
leadership positions, and a higher level of management
expertise were established in every practice that joined.

Within the same marketplaces, there were many groups
trying to accomplish the same success, often with deeper
financial and management resources; however, they were
consistently less successful. In fact, Medical Edge went
on to acquire some of these practices. And time after time

when these groups were included in the culture, they began to transform and perform at a higher level. It was more than new technology and new people. It was the new way employees related to the practice.

What was going on?

To my surprise, one aspect of the difference began with a five-foot-four-inch, redheaded dynamo named Suzan Oran. Suzan was the vice president of leadership development and had a commitment to empowering everyone at Medical Edge. Honestly, the first few times I met her, I found her remarkably annoying—upbeat, optimistic, and seemingly immune to drama and discouragement. Her can-do mentality seemed artificial and contrived compared to the "serious" doctor and leader that I considered myself to be. But try as I might, I could not get her to crack, to reveal some inauthentic, insincere actress under the bright exterior. As the chief medical and strategy officer, it was my job to work with the team to assess possible acquisitions, help the ones that joined, and make sure the quality and financial performance of each practice improved over time. In this capacity, I worked with Suzan regularly—initially with significant reservation and conflict, but eventually with great appreciation.

In retrospect, I believe I was a very typical product of our medical education system: extremely confident, evidence based, rational, linear, and driven, sure that working harder and smarter to push through challenges would inspire and drive higher performance from those around me. I was willing to work eighteen hours a day, and I was committed to a top-down, highly managed system where employees were to fill their roles and do as they were directed so the doctor could function at the highest possible level. Looking back, I can see that I had a single method for trying to succeed. It could be said I was a hammer looking for a nail to make sure I was successful and that Medical Edge was the best group in the United States. These are worthy goals, but I was committed to achieving them through an antiquated, misguided, and destined-to-fail methodology.

Suzan's coaching and workshops provided distinctions and concepts designed to empower individuals throughout Medical Edge to be highly collaborative, operate consistently with the mission/vision statement, and ultimately have successes that benefited everyone involved. The leadership team and staff used the workshops and coaching to sew the fabric of these concepts into the business and medical systems. Suzan led her five-level Empowerment program, Excellent Customer Service program, and Medical Practice Cohesive Team program, just to name a few, for several hundred employees. Over time, Suzan and I also worked together to provide a Creating New Possibilities program for the doctors, nurse practitioners, and physician's assistants. This was a renaissance for me in my life and for many of the providers with whom we worked. People were encouraged to participate in Suzan's workshops and to use the concepts and distinctions to benefit not only the overall business but also their personal lives. People had a real sense that the leadership team cared about them.

What you will find on the pages that follow is a collection of distinctions and concepts Suzan has gathered over the years and that she uses in her workshops and coaching. For those of us who have participated in her work, these are some of the seeds that were planted and continue to grow, providing a transformational way to lead a practice as well as to live a life.

It is with great excitement and expectation that we bring you this book. You may be ready to apply one or two of these suggestions—or you may be ready to methodically apply every suggestion over the next few months and create a breakthrough in your level of influence within your practice.

However you elect to use this book, we respect your choice and applaud your commitment and perseverance in pursuing the never-ending opportunity for improvement. We hope that you, too, experience great joy, wonderment, and success from the distinctions shared in the following pages.

Thank you for giving us the opportunity to share them with you!

Scott

Being a Medical Leader

Becoming a leader is synonymous with becoming yourself.
It is precisely that simple, and it is also that difficult.

Warren Bennis

The first step in having success is shifting your paradigm so that who you are *being*, which is what will shape and steer you going forward, is consistent with the success you are committed to having.

You're clearly committed to making a difference in people's lives. You've already dedicated yourself to contributing to people's health and wellbeing, and given that you've started this book, you're also interested in providing leadership that supports the success of your practice. You've likely discovered you have varying degrees of influence within the practice. For example, it may seem that you have less influence or that your focus has become more financial or less health-oriented than you expected when you began your career.

....

Common Leadership Mistake
Trying to do everything yourself

....

A medical practice cannot function without the entire team. An individual physician can always go back to practicing medicine door-to-door with his or her black bag, and that can be a beautiful way to make a difference. However, providing the kind of medical care a practice can offer requires the entire team.

Sometimes people forget (or maybe don't realize) that each person in a medical practice has an influence on the team—whether that person is a provider, nurse, medical assistant, receptionist, scheduler, technician, billing specialist, practice manager, etc.

When you provide effective leadership in your role (whatever role that is), you directly support the entire staff in being a cohesive team that can then make the biggest difference possible for your patients.

We intend to support you in that endeavor by providing ideas, concepts, and distinctions that you can apply to increase your leadership effectiveness and achieve a breakthrough in your level of influence. We will provide specific suggestions for identifying and shifting your leadership strategies to continually become more effective in the practice.

One person cannot do everything all the time, although some try. The need for overarching control inevitably limits the practice. Within the medical field, those in leadership positions often end up operating in an autocratic fashion instead of allowing a more inclusive system of productivity. This not only inhibits the functionality of the entire organization, but it also limits the ability of each person on the team to thrive, including the leader. Knowledge of some of the key distinctions in this book can help take leadership from a place of dominance and hierarchy to one of inspiration.

How the leader relates to team members is key. Many new leaders tend to think leadership is about telling people what to do. They erroneously believe that their authority to hire and fire will motivate people to do what the leader says. As you gain leadership experience, it will become clear that it's less about making all the decisions and telling people what to do and more about helping them discover what they could do to achieve the goals.

The premise of this book is that successful leadership is a function of having a powerful vision and then operating consistently within that vision by using effective relationship and communication skills. We assert that this is essential to leadership success and that these skills are available to everyone aspiring to become a successful leader.

In most fields, the only way a person establishes credibility as a leader is by first demonstrating extraordinary ability in the primary field of endeavor. Not having this kind of credibility makes the leader's job twice as difficult, if not impossible, in many organizations. Credibility has to be earned or granted before a person can truly be an effective leader.

Once in possession of this credibility, the developing

leader needs time to gain experience and self-knowledge. Before leaders can successfully gauge the strengths and weak spots of others, they must first become intimately familiar with and take into account their own. Self-knowledge, almost by definition, can be learned but not taught. It is achieved through a personal quest using a variety of approaches. These include personal development programs, communication and relationship workshops, executive coaching, psychotherapy, and so on. However, because some leaders don't purposefully set out to become leaders, they are in a sense "accidental leaders." And lacking any formal preparation for that role, they tend in the beginning to act only in accordance with their personalities. It is vital that they stay engaged in the courageous process of exploring and working with their personal strengths and weaknesses.

Many physicians acknowledge that they may not be the most highly socialized individuals or that they are often ill prepared for the job of being a leader. In the first place, medical training tends to equate leadership with having all the answers and dazzling colleagues and subordinates (especially subordinates) with one's intelligence and insightfulness. Not infrequently, this is done with an arrogant, condescending edge, and yet it's pretty much accepted as "how doctors are" in medical circles. Doctors as a group come out of college, medical school, and residency relatively poorly socialized, because while many of their nonmedical friends were drinking beer, hanging out, and "finding themselves" in college, they were in the library or hospital studying. Before they can become effective leaders, these overachievers generally have some work to do in the areas of self-awareness and beliefs about the world and other people.

In the beginning, new leaders are by necessity more inwardly focused and engaged in learning by trial and error. They often self-consciously question, and then second-guess, how to interact with subordinates—expending considerable energy determining the "right" course of action and whether they are being too lax or strict, too friendly or aloof.

Excellence in leadership means being able to see the previously unseen, hear the unspoken between the spoken words, read and interpret the nonverbal communications, and begin to intuit what is really going on. It is impossible to achieve this depth of understanding of the world around us until we have settled some of our internal challenges.

Unexamined beliefs will likely create unintended results. When you identify your current beliefs about leadership, your ability to effectively lead others, and any discrepancies with your commitment, you can then powerfully and newly declare who you will be as a leader.

Psychologist and author of *Emotional Intelligence* Daniel Goleman indirectly refers to the highest level of observational and intuitive ability (shared by extraordinary leaders, we believe) in the following quotation:

> *The range of what we think and do is limited by what we fail to notice. And because we fail to notice that we fail to notice, there is little we can do to change until we notice how failing to notice shapes our thoughts and deeds.*

Some might call this aspect of leadership "wisdom." We agree and suggest the access to that wisdom may live in a rich set of distinctions about relationships, communication, intentionality, and vision.

These distinctions enable leaders to see things they were unable to see before and to intuit more as well. Whatever we term this essential aspect of leadership, it's clear there is a never-ending opportunity to develop these qualities.

Spectacular leadership successes have been achieved through many different styles and approaches. Is it possible there's no common skill set shared by successful leaders? And if that's the case, how can anyone learn to become a successful leader, short of simply mimicking someone else's approach?

We assert that successful leaders do share a common set of skills—although they might not be immediately apparent to observers or even to the individuals themselves—and that their success has everything to do with who the leaders are *being*, rather than with their individual styles of leadership.

Fundamental Distinction: Be—Do—Have

People tend to begin their journey in leadership (or any journey) wanting to *have* success. To get this success, we usually focus first on what to *do* to achieve that end. Ultimately leadership success (and success in all endeavors) lies in *who we are being*. This can be a challenging concept to grasp.

Typically, in the desire to have what we want to have, we focus on what we need to do to produce that result, often skipping entirely the inquiry into who we're being. This book will provide many distinctions and suggestions to support you in taking action and doing what's next to produce the results you are committed to having.

However, the first step in having success is shifting your paradigm so that who you are being, which is what will shape and steer you going forward, is consistent with the success you are committed to. It requires a willingness to take a stand and be consistent with what you are committed to, even though it is not yet reality.

This concept is rarely talked about in business; however, it is a standard element of preparation and is considered mandatory for many elite athletes. It was previously called visualization and is now typically referred to as imagery. For example, a downhill skier might sit on a chair in her hotel room and envision herself skiing down the entire run—she can hear it, smell it, and feel it, and can see each section of the run in her mind's eye. Dr. JoAnn Dahlkoetter provides sports psychology coaching in her book *Your Performing Edge: The Total Mind-Body Program for Excellence in Sports, Business, and Life.*[1]

These concepts are starting to become less rare in both business and medicine. There is a unique, high-level course titled Being a Leader and the Effective Exercise of Leadership: An Ontological/Phenomenological Model by Werner Erhard, Michael C. Jensen, and Kari L. Granger.

---

1   Dr. JoAnn Dahlkoetter, *Your Performing Edge: The Total Mind-Body Program for Excellence in Sports, Business, and Life*, 4th ed. (San Carlos, CA: Pulgas Ridge Press, 2007). Dr. Dahlkoetter has been a medical staff member at Stanford University Medical Center for ten years. As a sports psychologist and performance coach, she is one of America's most in-demand performance consultants and a world-class athlete whose clients include several Olympic gold medalists.

This course has been taught at several universities, including the Geisel School of Medicine at Dartmouth in June 2012 and the University of British Columbia in June 2013.

"The ontological model of leader and leadership opens up and reveals the *actual* nature of being when one is being a leader and opens up and reveals the source of *one's actions* when exercising leadership," according to the authors' working paper "Creating Leaders: An Ontological Model." An abstract of the paper is available at Harvard Business School's Working Knowledge website.[2]

We invite you to envision what your practice will look like when it becomes the full success to which you're committed. Envision your patient volume as you want it to be. Envision your practice with a full staff that is well trained, is passionate about caring for your patients, and enjoys coming to work. Envision how you arrive in the morning and greet your staff and patients. Envision how you interact with your staff when a challenge arises. Envision how you acknowledge your staff for a job well done. And then be that person now. *Act as if your goal has already been achieved.*

Be what you want others around you to be (reliable, efficient, timely, communicative, enthusiastic, open-minded, etc.). Act like the leader of an extremely successful medical practice. And when something goes awry, treat it not as a problem, but as an opportunity to improve.

---

2   Werner Erhard, Michael C. Jensen, and Kari L. Granger, "Creating Leaders: An Ontological Model." (Working Paper No. 11-037, Harvard Business School, October 2010), http://ssrn.com/abstract=1681682.

Begin today to act as, live as, and *be* the person you would be if you had already achieved your goal. How would you carry yourself? What would you focus on? How would you treat yourself? How would you treat other people? What would your relationships be like? When you are being a leader, you no longer have to prove anything with respect to leadership. This allows you to be passionately caring and have fun at the same time.

Be—Do—Have
Paradigm Shift

Automatic Human Tendency

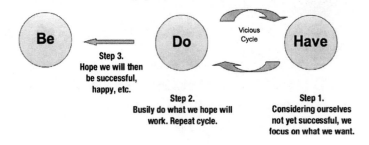

Step 3.
Hope we will then be successful, happy, etc.

Vicious Cycle

Step 2.
Busily do what we hope will work. Repeat cycle.

Step 1.
Considering ourselves not yet successful, we focus on what we want.

Intentional Way of Being

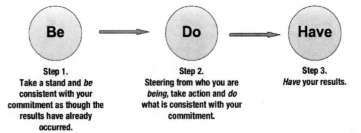

Step 1.
Take a stand and *be* consistent with your commitment as though the results have already occurred.

Step 2.
Steering from who you are *being*, take action and *do* what is consistent with your commitment.

Step 3.
Have your results.

This is a shift from the vicious cycle of our automatic human tendency to busily do more in hopes that we'll have the results we want

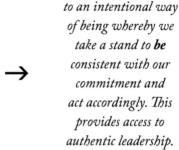

*to an intentional way of being whereby we take a stand to **be** consistent with our commitment and act accordingly. This provides access to authentic leadership.*

The following exercises will support you in applying and gaining maximum value from this distinction.

Practice

1.   Fill in the three-column list provided (or start your own notebook).

2.   Catch yourself whenever you are not ***being*** consistent with the success of your practice, and intentionally shift. (Resist the tendency to be critical of yourself—just make the shift. Your progress will now be turbocharged.)

3.   Refer to this list as you read the book, and look for the distinctions that will have a positive impact on your success in these three areas.

As a leader ...

Who do you want to **be**?	What do you want to **do**?	What do you want to **have**?
_____	_____	_____
_____	_____	_____
_____	_____	_____
_____	_____	_____

How Are You Relating to Others?

In times of change, learners inherit the earth, while the learned find themselves beautifully equipped to deal with a world that no longer exists.

Eric Hoffer

> What if one of the key factors in people's ability to rise to the occasion and excel is how those around them, particularly their leader(s), are relating to them?

Leaders are only as effective as the people with whom they surround themselves. This is a law of leadership that is essential to understand, accept, and respect. To begin this part of the journey, let's start with the primary question: how do you think of and relate to the other people in your practice? Next, which do you think comes first—how others perform around you, or how you relate to them? Or are the two completely interrelated?

Have you ever been in a situation where you were talking

or working with someone and it seemed you couldn't think straight or do anything right—or conversely, a situation where you were working with someone and were easily performing at your best? What if one of the key factors in people's ability to rise to the occasion and excel is how those around them, particularly their leader(s), are relating to them?

Whenever you begin a new relationship, whether it's with a physician, staff member, or patient, the distinctions in this chapter can set the tone for an extraordinary relationship from the beginning. We assert that applying these distinctions to your existing relationships will also effect a significant positive shift.

When you look at your organization, what do you see around you? Is everyone empowered and activated? How are you at fostering and encouraging the people around you? Have you taken the lessons you learned in your medical training and applied them to the practice? If so, there's a good chance this may be holding back your leadership success. Two foundational distinctions will support you in maximizing your effectiveness as a leader: *listening for* people and maintaining an open mind by *being a learner.*

First, let's examine communication. Communication can easily be broken down into two parts: speaking and listening. The speaking part is very important, and throughout this book we will provide many suggestions for effectiveness in that part of the conversation. We suggest, however, that the listening part plays the more powerful role in effective communication.

Example:

1. I'm talking with you, I'm articulate, and I express things beautifully—but if you're not powerfully listening, we cannot have effective communication.

2. I'm talking with you, and I stumble over my words or struggle to say what I want to express—but if you are powerfully listening, we can have effective communication.

Most conversations are simply monologues delivered in the presence of a witness.

Margaret Millar

We all know it's important to be a good listener, and we all know how much we appreciate it when someone is really listening when we talk.

The greatest compliment that was ever paid me was when one asked me what I thought, and attended to my answer.

Henry David Thoreau

However, as often as we plan (sometimes even writing out) what we are going to say during an important discussion, how often do we plan how we will listen during the discussion? Let's explore some strategies for listening attentively.

Being a Good Listener

- Actually paying attention to the person and what is being said

- Making eye contact if you are speaking in person

- Not interrupting

- Nodding your head or saying "uh-huh" to let the other person know you are still paying attention

- Asking clarifying questions without steering the conversation to your agenda

- Recapping what the other person has said

Being a Powerful Listener

Being a powerful listener increases the opportunity for those around you to excel. This includes practicing all the skills listed above, plus two distinctions that can transform your relationships: *listening for* the other person and being a *learner* in the conversation.

Distinction: Listening For versus Listening About

When someone is audibly speaking a language we understand and we're paying attention, we say we are listening. And we are, to a degree. Our automatic tendency is to listen through a filter of judgment: Do I agree or disagree? Do I like what's being said? Do I think what's being said is "right" or "wrong?" Do I think what's being said makes sense? If it doesn't, do I think the other person is wrong for not explaining it better, or that I'm wrong for not understanding?

None of this is planned. We suggest it is an automatic element of being human—our "default listening mode." We call this kind of listening *listening about*. There is nothing wrong with this level of listening. In fact, many of us have had a fair amount of success in life with this kind of listening.

However, we suggest there's a new option for building connection and increasing productivity: *listening for*. This means listening for who the other person is and for his or her commitment. We absorb what's being said yet also listen beyond that to focus on who this person really is and what's important to him.

Listening for will open up communication and likely foster the opportunity for others to excel around you. When we *listen for* the other person, we are respecting who she is and her role (whether or not we agree with or like what is being said). Later we will explore examples of how this affects relationships.

Included in the distinction *listening for* is another distinction called *honoring people's commitment*.

....

Common Leadership Mistake

Questioning people's commitment to their jobs or to the practice—thinking people who do what you want are committed to the practice and people who don't are not committed to the practice

....

Distinction: Honoring People's Commitment

We are using the following definition for *commitment*: "The state of being bound emotionally or intellectually to a course of action or to another person or persons; the state or instance of being emotionally impelled (as in a commitment to a cause)."

We all have many different areas of commitment. We have commitments to our own wellbeing, to expressing ourselves and being heard, to making a difference, and to our careers, marriages, families, communities, churches, volunteer work, projects, etc.

We strongly encourage you never to question anyone's commitment. That is a bold statement because when you really stop and look, you realize you regularly question people's commitment. Sometimes this doubt is voiced out loud, but frequently, we doubt and question people's commitment in our own inner conversations.

We strongly encourage you to actually give people the benefit of the doubt. Is this just being naïve, or will it, in fact, increase productivity? Does this tap into some underlying wisdom that leads to greater connection in relationships?

To answer these questions, we begin by making the following assertions regarding commitment:

Assertion 1: As human beings, we are all, at our core, fundamentally committed to loving others and being loved. We all have a commitment to excellence. People want to make a difference while they are on this planet. We all have a commitment to having relationships that work for the other person as well as for ourselves.

Assertion 2: Our actions and words are distinct from our commitment. Our actions and words may or may not be consistent with and foster our commitment. We make choices about our actions and words every waking hour.

Assertion 3: You can never definitively know what another person is committed to. You cannot scientifically prove, measure, or do lab work to verify what a person is committed to. You can never know with 100 percent certainty whether someone is really committed to his or her job, to the medical practice, to a spouse or children, and so on, but our human tendency is to look at people's actions and words to try to determine their commitment.

Assertion 4: We have all acted inconsistently with our commitment at times (been late for work, been close-minded and missed out on a solution someone was offering, gotten behind on our paperwork or reports, yelled at our kids, not exercised, etc.).

Assertion 5: People do not intentionally underperform or cause problems in their lives. We don't believe people sit on the sides of their beds in the morning and plan out the day by thinking, "Today, mediocrity. Yes, today I will go for mediocrity. I will do the least amount of work possible to get by. If others have to pick up my slack, fine." Or, "Today I will stir up turmoil and drama. Yeah, that's good. I'll see what problems I can create for others. Yes, now I'm ready to start my day."

In case you are tempted to tune out this message, let us be clear: We know there are people (such as those experiencing depression or deep grief, built-up anger, etc.) who might be having these types of thoughts. We also know there are people (ourselves included) who have, at times, operated at a level of mediocrity. We have all dropped the ball before. We have all stirred up drama and created problems for ourselves as well as others in our lives. We have all done stuff that didn't work.

We suggest that when humans do that, it isn't because they're intentionally designing their lives that way. There is something else going on that's overshadowing their commitment to excellence. When that's left unexamined and not tended to, it becomes a pattern in their lives. So this leaves us with the assertion that at the deepest level, people really are committed to excellence.

Assertion 6: People feel known and respected when their commitment is not questioned but instead honored. We are all more open to looking at and discussing what's not working when we're not being triggered to defend ourselves or shut down. And knowing you can directly address someone else's actions without condemning the person makes it more likely you will have that conversation sooner and in a far more effective way.

Here are some examples of how this distinction would look in real relationships.

Questioning Someone's Commitment

Bob is married and has two amazing children. He's a busy executive and travels a lot. As his kids have grown, his business travel has increased. One day his wife, Betty, says, "Bob, you haven't called the kids lately. You get most of your updates about them from me. Don't you even care about what's going on in their lives? Don't you care about your relationship with them? Gosh, I thought you wanted to be a good dad!"

If you were Bob, how would you feel? Attacked, guilty, burdened? Would you second-guess yourself as a dad? What is the quality of your partnership with your spouse at that moment? Would you be inclined to defend yourself and explain why you haven't talked with the kids lately? Would you be inclined to focus more on how you felt attacked by your wife rather than what actions you could take to make a positive difference going forward?

Standing For Someone's Commitment

What if instead Betty had said, "Bob, I know you are very committed to your relationship with the kids. They love to share with you and hear about what's going on with your business trips and your life. I noticed you haven't called them lately. They would love to hear from you."

If you were Bob, would this be empowering and supportive for you and your relationship with your kids and your wife?

Now let's take this right into your medical practice.

Sally is Dr. Smith's medical assistant. She's been arriving to work late on occasion, and it's now happening more often. The practice manager, Donna, is talking with Dr. Smith about her upcoming meeting with Sally.

Questioning Someone's Commitment

Donna says, "This is getting to be a real problem. I don't know what to do with Sally. She seems to think she can just get away with coming in late. She's not a team player. If she were, she would realize that when she comes in late, everyone else has to cover for her. I think we have to let her go, but that's going to mean added work for me to replace her. I just hate these personnel issues! Why can't people act like adults?"

Dr. Smith says, "Well, she seems to be a pretty good

MA, but maybe she really isn't committed to her job. I hate to see time and energy wasted dealing with this stuff. You figure it out."

Donna then meets with Sally and says, "Dr. Smith and I have talked, and we don't think you're committed to your job and being a team player. You coming in late to work is a problem for all of us."

Sally now looks upset. Donna feels bad, plus she's worried about the increased work to replace Sally. So she reverts to the reaction she often relies upon to avoid feeling bad—she backs down. "Well, anyway, we have a full schedule of patients today," she says. "Just try to be on time in the future. Let's get back to work."

Later, she follows up with Dr. Smith. "Dr. Smith, I spoke with Sally about her being late. I think it's going to be OK." (Notice nothing was really settled.)

If you were Sally, how would you feel? Embarrassed, guilty, invalidated? Would you be confused by the mixed message of the practice manager starting off harsh and then ending without resolution? Would you feel more self-conscious in your relationship with the doctor and the rest of the staff?

At this point, what is the nature of Sally's relationship with Dr. Smith, her practice manager, and the entire staff? We suggest that Sally is less likely to excel in this work environment than she was before these conversations.

Standing For Someone's Commitment

What if instead Donna said, "Dr. Smith, I wanted you to know I will be meeting with Sally today to discuss her arriving late in the mornings. As we both know, she is a good medical assistant, really cares about your patients, and wants to have success in her life. I believe she will turn this around. I certainly hope so—I would hate to lose her for a variety of reasons. I'll let you know how the conversation went after the meeting."

Then in the meeting, Donna says, "Sally, thanks for coming in. I know you really care about the patients here and have a commitment to doing a great job. You have a lot of talent and skills that make a difference in our practice. I want to have a straight conversation about one area that's not working, though: your tardiness in the mornings. I know it doesn't happen every day; however, when you are late, it adds extra work for the rest of the staff and starts the day with us running behind. It's important for this practice that you be on time. Please share with me your commitment to being on time. What will you do to turn that around?"

And after a respectful discussion, she says, "Sally, thank you for your commitment to excellence, including arriving on time. I really appreciate all you do here for our patients! Let's meet together in two weeks and evaluate how everything is going at that point."

Listening for people is a gift that we give others as well as ourselves. It requires an intention to fully hear what other people are saying and *listen for* their underlying commitments.

This does not come naturally for any of us. When we design our listening specifically for that purpose, training ourselves to take in all aspects of the other person's communication (words, body language, tone of voice, and what's not being said) and honoring the person's underlying commitments, we can develop a very rich relationship.

The Ego

Let's talk for a moment about our egos. The definition we are using for "ego" is our automatic tendency to want to be right, look good, avoid domination by others, and survive. We all have an ego, but it's not who we really are. And although we will never get rid of our egos, we can catch ourselves when our egos are driving our thoughts and actions. At those moments, we can intentionally shift to thinking and acting in accordance with our commitment to relationships and endeavors that work well for everyone involved.

The problem with the ego is that it's typically expressed through what Fred Kofman calls "toxic thoughts."[1] These are our negative judgments, assessments, and conclusions about ourselves, others, and situations. Ego-based thinking and behavior locks us into the "us versus them" mentality. It is important for us to be honest with ourselves and acknowledge that we all do this from time to time.

A powerful distinction that can be used to deepen our relationships and significantly increase our leadership effectiveness is to set our egos aside and let our commitment steer our conversations and actions.

---

1   Fred Kofman, *Conscious Business: How to Build Value Through Value* (Boulder: Sounds True, 2006).

Distinction: Being a *Learner* versus Being a *Knower*

If you're continually keeping up with medicine and continuing your education, then you're a *learner*, right? Actually, no. This is not a reference to knowledge. This distinction refers to your predominant way of addressing challenges when they occur—your mindset or attitude. You can be quite knowledgeable about a topic and even be in a teaching role, yet at the same time have the mindset of a *learner—which is exactly what we are encouraging*. When you have a keen awareness of yourself, you can recognize when you are being a *knower* and shift to being a *learner* multiple times per day.

Knowers, according to Fred Kofman, have that "know-it-all" attitude. They give free rein to their toxic thoughts. As we have said, toxic thoughts are normal for all of us; however, the effective leader will find a way to address them in himself and his team members.

Kofman says, "Don't dump the toxic thoughts or swallow them, but rather learn to 'detoxify' them and express them in a different way that can contribute to the group's progress." You have an opportunity to actually catch yourself having the toxic or disempowering thought, and to then stop and remind yourself of your commitment to the relationship, group, and goals. Think of a way to rephrase the thought so it is honest and empowering.

This takes time, energy, and creativity. We believe it's very well worth it! You will save so much time by reducing upsets—including the time spent engaged in the upset and the time spent cleaning it up. You and your group can experience what it's like to be a cohesive team in which people are open to problem-solving together and supporting one another.

As an example, a *knower* may say, "That project will never work." The comment is delivered as if it were expressing absolute fact, when in reality it is just that person's opinion. It may be a very logical and well-constructed opinion, but it is opinion nevertheless. The underlying toxic thought is, "I'm right. You're wrong." Detoxified, a more authentic way to express the thought would be, "I have some concerns that the project won't work."

When we are *being learners*, we view the world from a different perspective.

Knower	Learner
Criticizes others and self	Gives people the benefit of the doubt
Lets toxic thoughts permeate thought/ expression	Detoxifies negative thoughts prior to expression
Focuses on being proven right	Is open to explore what will work
Has the attitude "I know, and I am right"	Has the attitude "I have ideas and opinions"
Resists feedback—is rigid and positional	Is open to constructive criticism/input
Tries to control the situation	Focuses on being influential in solving the challenge
Feels saving face is important	Is psychologically secure and willing to admit mistakes
Believes, "I am my thoughts"	Believes, "I am a thinking person"
Sees problems as persecution and attack	Embraces challenges as the next step in the process
Needs to solve or be saved from the problem	Embraces collaboration with colleagues
Thinks and acts based on fear	Thinks and acts based on commitment/ love

When we are being *learners,* we approach interactions in life as learning opportunities. We have no preconceptions about how things will turn out and are authentically interested in all opinions on the subject. We believe the group will succeed by working together, sharing ideas, and shifting toxic thoughts. We are happy to lose face and acknowledge our mistakes because we know there is freedom in not needing to protect our egos and that we will gain knowledge in the process. We can say, "I was wrong. Thank you for letting me know. Now that we know that doesn't work, we can move on to the next learning opportunity."

A leader who's being a *knower* will lead a team in a closed, protective manner that causes others to feel hesitant to participate and offer new ideas. The team members will either focus on being liked by and trying to please the leader or on rebelling.

A leader who's being a *learner* will lead a team in an open, inclusive manner that supports others in feeling confident, empowered, and inspired to participate and contribute.

Making this shift in mindset can be one of the biggest challenges and one of the most rewarding changes we make in our lives. The book *The Power of TED* (*The Empowerment Dynamic™)*[2] by David Emerald is a simple parable that highlights this transformation and points to

---

2 David Emerald, *The Power of TED* (*The Empowerment Dynamic™)* (Bainbridge Island: Polaris, 2006); David Emerald and Scott Conard, MD, *TED* (*The Empowerment Dynamic™) for Diabetes: A Health Empowerment Story* (Bainbridge Island: Polaris, 2012).

the power of being a *learner*. *TED** beautifully illustrates the shift any of us can make at any moment from being a victim (meaning we feel stuck and "at the effect" of a person or situation) to being a creator (meaning we cultivate our capacities to create outcomes). A *creator* increases her ability to choose a response to life circumstances (even in the hardest of situations) rather than merely reacting to them. They call this "making shift happen!"

Key Point

We will forever find ourselves at times *listening about* and being *knowers*. Don't criticize yourself (that is just more of being a knower). Simply catch yourself and intentionally shift to listening for the other person and being a *learner*. You have a never-ending opportunity to shift so that your communication and connection with others is open, productive, and empowering.

Practice

1. Review your Be, Do, Have list from chapter 1. Are things starting to naturally fall into place for some of your items? Remember to focus on what you want, not what you don't want.

2. For the next week, notice when your attention drifts while others are talking. Notice when you are *listening about* (merely focusing on whether you like or agree with what the other person is saying), and then shift to *listening for* the other person (*listen for* the person's commitment, give her the benefit of the doubt, and listen from her point of view).

3. For the next week, notice when you're being a knower (only truly open to other people's point of view if they agree with you), and then shift to being a *learner.*

4. Note the positive impact this has in your relationships. Reinforcing others' commitment will be inspiring and will increase productivity for them as well as you.

Do You Have a Solid Foundation for Your Practice?

Vision without action is a daydream. Action without vision is a nightmare.

Japanese Proverb

> Have a purpose-driven practice. How to collaboratively create a powerful and living mission/vision statement that shapes the culture of your practice.

Do you ever think some of your practice's efforts are scattered?

Do you or members of your staff ever feel you're nearing burnout?

Does it ever seem as if you have conflicting office procedures?

Do you have ideas about how to move your practice forward but can't decide which ones to implement?

Do you ever feel as though your ideas for the practice might meet opposition, so why bother?

If any of this is true for you, it may be a function of not having the purpose of your practice clearly identified and alive within the team.

What is the purpose of your medical practice? The answer may seem obvious; however, we have found the first answer to this question usually doesn't capture the rich depth of what you really want and envision.

Why Use Your Time to Create a Mission/Vision Statement for Your Practice?

Involving your entire team in creating a mission/vision statement that represents the true purpose of your practice provides a solid foundation. In addition to representing your commitment to excellent medical care for your patients, your mission/vision statement will include your commitment to excellence as a team, both within the practice and with other medical providers as well as your business practices. This statement is one of the primary building blocks for creating a *culture in your practice* that's consistent with your commitment!

> *Create a compelling vision, one that takes people to a new place, and then translate that vision into a reality.*
>
> Warren Bennis

....

Common Leadership Mistake
Not clarifying on a regular basis what the ultimate purpose of the practice is

....

Distinction: Mission/Vision

Vision

A vision is like a lighthouse. It illuminates rather than limits, gives direction rather than destination. A vision is a consciously created image of what you would like the organization to be—a waking dream. A vision comes from the heart. It touches, moves, and inspires people to action whether anyone is watching or not. A vision of greatness will focus on service and on adding value to and empowering others. A great vision statement inspires commitment because it is worth pursuing for its own sake.

The vision may not necessarily be considered practical or reasonable. The loftiness of a vision may seem to ask too much of you. If it does, then you're on the right track. Great visions are not handed down from above, nor are they dictatorial or manipulative. They are created, crafted, and shaped in partnership with those who will be living the vision. *Involving each person in the organization in the creation of the vision is an act of leadership that fosters a cohesive team.* When people experience being a part of the design, they are naturally drawn to operate in ways that are consistent with that design.

Mission

A mission statement is a statement of what the business is—it defines the nature and scope of the business. A mission statement tells people about your organization's technical competence, what you will provide for your employees, what you will provide for your patients, and what you've set out to contribute.

When a group does not have a powerful mission/vision statement or doesn't actually use its mission/vision statement, the organization is steered by the personalities and coping mechanisms of the individuals in it. This makes for inconsistencies and creates the struggle to get people to fall in line.

Without a mission/vision statement, we often get caught up in the day-to-day tasks of our busy schedules and lose sight of the bigger picture. When we're not in touch with our purpose and the difference we're making, we miss the opportunity to experience joy in our work, and this can create a downward spiral toward burnout.

Why Use Your Staff's Time to Participate in This Process?

At many companies, hospitals, and medical groups, the mission/vision statement is written by the owner, top leadership group, or, quite often, the marketing department. A more compelling and successful method is to include everyone in the process. When everyone on the team participates, they help create a personally relevant and inspiring mission/vision statement for your practice.

The Benefits of Involving Your Entire Team in Creating Your Statement

- Collaborating as a team to create something important for the practice fosters cohesiveness and team spirit.

- When team members know their voices matter and will be used to support the practice, it naturally encourages them to give their all.

- When team members are giving their all more often, the practice will benefit in unpredictable ways.

Team members are far more likely to respect and live by the statement if they were part of creating it.

Ideas for Creating or Revising Your Mission/Vision Statement

There's a lot of good information available to support you and your team in creating or revising your mission statement. Many organizations find using a consultant or facilitator to guide this process adds great value. There are many different formats you can use depending on your personal preference. It can be useful to read other organizations' mission/vision statements that you find well done or inspiring. Reading several of these examples to your group can open everyone's minds to what's possible. It can help you decide whether you want to create separate sections for your mission, vision, and values or whether you'd like to combine them as one message. Once you've read these examples to the group once or twice, put them away, and take care not to copy them or allow them to limit what you can create for your own practice.

The Statement Design Process

This seven-step process usually takes three to six weeks. This is not something that should be rushed. It's much more important to include every physician and staff member in the process. On the other hand, it's also important not to let the process drag out too long or be dropped. As a leader in your practice, stay very involved in the process without dominating it. Empower others to manage the process while you act as more of an active participant.

Step 1: Hold an Initial Group Meeting (See Suggested Agenda Below)

Hold a group meeting that includes everyone in the practice. Set aside one to two hours for this meeting. Acknowledge team members' commitment to the practice, encourage them each to be involved in the process, and let them know their input is valuable. Select a mission/vision statement steering committee of three to five people. Collect everyone's ideas so the steering committee can use them for the first draft.

Step 2: Hold a Steering Committee Meeting

1. Committee members create a first draft of the mission statement.

2. They submit the draft to all employees with a cover memo outlining the process, asking for their input, and giving a date to have their sug-

gestions for the second draft back to the committee.

Step 3: Encourage Participation

The steering committee and management gently encourage employees to submit their ideas and acknowledge them when they do. If some people participate less than others, remember to give them the benefit of the doubt and invite them individually to participate. If they still don't get involved, let it go. The fact that they had the opportunity has already been a benefit.

Step 4: Hold a Second Steering Committee Meeting

1. Create a second draft from everyone's input.

2. Submit this draft to all employees for any additional input, and give a date for returning it. (This step can be repeated three or four times until you have your statement).

Step 5: Verify Alignment at the Top

Verify that the top organizational leaders (the owner of the company, top management, etc.) are fully aligned with and stand behind this mission/vision statement.

Step 6: Announce and Celebrate Your Statement

When you have finalized the mission/vision statement, have a meeting/party to announce and celebrate your statement. Brainstorm how you will use the statement to maximize its value. Continue to remind everyone to think of this statement as the foundation for the practice, not as a goal to reach someday.

Suggested Agenda for
Initial Group Meeting

- Acknowledge team members' commitment to the practice.

- Remind them that they each make a unique contribution to the practice and that you really want everyone to be involved in creating your mission/vision statement.

- Ask everyone to *listen for* one another and be *learners* in this process.

- Review the design process steps listed above so everyone will understand how it works and be included.

- Select a mission/vision statement steering committee of three to five people.

- Write the answers to the following questions on a flip chart:

    * Who are we, and what do we do? (Encourage everyone to participate. Keep asking, "What else? Who are we as a group and what do we do?")

    * When talking with family or friends, what do you say you are most proud of or thankful for in this practice?

    * What are some of the important qualities we stand for?

    * What do our patients say is unique about us?

- Now go back through the above questions again, but look at them from the perspective of patients, potential employees, and other physicians.

- Close your meeting by thanking everyone for their participation.

Step 7: Make Your Statement a Working Document and Keep It Alive in Your Practice

Position framed copies in several locations around your practice, including the waiting room. Make it one of the first things you review with people being interviewed to join the practice. Feature it on the first page of your employee handbook. Post it on your website, and include it in written materials that represent your practice. Read it out loud at the beginning of important meetings. When there are challenges or conflicts, reread the statement and use it to support you and your team in taking appropriate action. Beyond printing it, posting it, and preaching it, practice what is expressed in your the mission and vision—actually live it. Lead by example. Any time you or others are operating inconsistently with the statement—and there will be such times—acknowledge it, clean it up, and get back on track. Using the mission/vision statement on a regular basis and in a meaningful way shapes the culture of your practice.

Ultimately when this process is complete, you'll have a statement that is clear, inspiring, energizing, and beneficial to people inside and outside your organization. This statement will evoke your group's pride and excitement about being part of something bigger than their individual roles.

- Schedule the first steering committee meeting.

- Agree on the date that everyone will receive the first draft from the steering committee and the timeline for the rest of the process.

- Thank everyone for their participation and for all they do day in, day out to make a difference in people's health and wellbeing!

You'll know you've been successful with this seven-step process when you see a new level of expressed commitment and excitement from your employees. Instead of feeling as though they're just cogs in a wheel and told what to do, staff members will have a sense of ownership and vitality. Conversations that were previously tedious and mundane will become opportunities for people to share the vision and live out the purpose of the practice as well as their individual purposes at work. They will begin to bring an energy and commitment to their jobs that no financial incentive could create. With this foundation, you will find many of the frustrations and setbacks you were experiencing (such as those mentioned at the beginning of this chapter) begin to disappear.

You will also begin to transform your role from a driving force to an inspiring leader who models, encourages, and supports the vision of living with purpose instead of going through the motions to get a paycheck. When you combine this with your ongoing commitment to *listen for* new ideas and suggestions and to always remain a *learner*, innovative ideas will continue to emerge from those working beside you, and you'll live out your mission and vision for service.

Practice

1. Review your Be, Do, Have list. Continue to focus on what you want, not what you don't want.

2. Continue to *listen for* others and be a *learner*. Shift your thinking anytime you catch yourself being rigid and closed-minded with a "my-way-is-the-right-way" attitude.

3. If you don't have a mission/vision statement for your practice, talk with your practice manager and the other physicians in your practice and make plans to have your entire group participate in creating one. Use the format in this chapter for support in this powerful process.

4. If your practice has a mission/vision statement that was created long ago, use our process to create a new statement. (We recommend reviewing your statement for possible revisions every two to four years.)

5. If you have a mission/vision statement that is meaningful and resonates with your practice, congratulations! Have a meeting with your group to highlight how the statement is currently being used to provide inspiration and direction. Ask the group to share ideas for new ways you can make this a working document for the practice.

Rally the Troops

True leaders don't create followers... They create more leaders!

Tom Peters

> Create an environment where your staff members are fully engaged and you will see an increase in improved medical outcomes for your patients.

Do your staff members say they're doing more than their fair share?

Do you ever think you are doing more than your fair share?

Do you hear staff members say, "No one told me we were doing that"?

Do you look back at the end of the day and think, "We could have been much more efficient with our time?"

Do you and your staff sometimes engage in office gossip, even though you know it divides the team?

Does it ever feel as though your practice is understaffed, even though your staff ratio is considered appropriate?

Wouldn't you love to have your practice operate like a well-oiled machine?

Imagine a practice where

- everything fits together, and there's a flow to what everyone is doing;

- people know their jobs and do them well;

- people focus on excelling at their jobs while also co-operating with others so that everyone excels; and

- people take pride in their individual accomplishments, yet the group accomplishments mean the most to everyone.

Think back to a time when you were part of a cohesive team. Do you know how it happened, how to re-create it, and more importantly, how to maintain it? It may seem elusive; however, it is possible for you to transform your practice into a harmonious and highly effective team. Creating an environment where your staff members are fully engaged in their jobs is an important part of the art of leadership.

> *Employee engagement strategies enable people to be the best they can at work, recognizing that this can only happen if they feel respected, involved, heard, well led, and valued by those they work for and with—"employee engagement is when the business values the employee and the employee values the business." Engaged employees have a sense of personal attachment to their work and organisation; they are motivated and able to give of their best to help it succeed—*

and from that flows a series of tangible benefits for the organisation and individuals alike.

—David MacLeod and Nita Clarke[1]

In this chapter, we'll add more distinctions and suggestions to support you in keeping the lines of communication open, keeping people informed, and engaging them in full participation individually and collectively. You will also learn about several common leadership mistakes.

Unfortunately, leaders often unknowingly divide their teams. Let's look at an example. Could this happen in your office?

Marie answers the phone. "Dr. Smith's office, this is Marie. How can I help you?"

Claire Jones says, "I'm furious, and I don't feel good. I called yesterday morning asking for a nurse to call me back. The medicine Dr. Smith prescribed for me on Monday is making me feel worse. You said the nurse would call me back, and she hasn't. Don't you guys even care about me unless I'm standing in your office?"

Marie replies, "I'm sorry the nurse hasn't called you back. I gave her the message yesterday right after you called."

"Well, I haven't heard from anyone! I need to talk with someone right now!" Claire exclaims in an angry tone.

Marie transfers the call to the nurse, who says, "Hello,

1   David MacLeod and Nita Clarke, "Engaging for Success: Enhancing Performance through Employee Engagement; A Report to Government," *Department for Business, Innovation and Skills* (2009), http://www.bis.gov.uk, Crown Copyright, BIS/ Pub 8859/07/09NP. URN09/1.

Mrs. Jones. This is Dr. Smith's nurse, Karen. I understand you have a problem. What can I do for you?" Karen's tone is irritated, and she proceeds to explain how busy their schedule has been.

When Claire saw Dr. Smith on Monday, she was diagnosed with high cholesterol, and Dr. Smith prescribed Zocor. When he said good-bye to Claire, he told her to call the office if she had any questions or problems with the new medication. She was pleased with her appointment with Dr. Smith. After starting the medication, she started feeling bad. She thought she was being reasonable by waiting over twenty-four hours before calling the office a second time.

Marie likes her job at the front desk and really cares about the patients. It is not rare for the nurse to fail to call patients back before they become upset. Marie has tried talking with her practice manager about it, but it hasn't helped. The practice manager seems to focus only on how important it is for Marie to be a team player and not be critical of other staff members. Marie feels caught between wanting to help the patients and not wanting to seem as though she's against the other staff members. Marie even brought the problem up with Dr. Smith, but he was quick to say that his nurse, Karen, was busy and that Marie just didn't understand.

Let us point out several dynamics in this scenario that lead to mediocrity in the practice:

- Dr. Smith feels frustrated that he seems to get a lot of patients who start out nice and then act like jerks. He feels a need to protect his nurse. He doesn't know what he would do without her. He also wonders why there is so much drama among his staff.

- Claire is now being treated like she's a problem patient. She thought Dr. Smith was going to be a caring doctor. She read in the new-patient packet that this office was a "patient medical home." She thought that sounded great. Now she doesn't really trust Dr. Smith in the same way. Does he truly have her best interests at heart? She's not sure anymore.

- Over time, Marie is learning to become numb to patient upsets so she can tolerate her job. Although she still cares about the patients, her cynicism is building.

- Karen has started gossiping about Marie to the other staff members and saying Marie doesn't work that hard.

All of this could have been avoided if the situation had been effectively addressed in a staff meeting. The topic of patients' calls not being returned in a timely manner could have been brought up as a question of what's not working rather than who's not working. The meeting could have been facilitated as an open and respectful exchange of ideas. Team members would then have had the opportunity to come up with a realistic system for providing excellent customer service to the patients. They could have rallied together to make the new system work.

Six Keys to Having a Cohesive, Inspired, and Fully Engaged Team

1. The purpose for the practice is clear.

People rally together when they're doing something meaningful. Every single person working in a medical practice makes a huge difference! In the midst of a busy office, this is often forgotten. Given that each staff member is a reflection of the physician, we assert that each person's actions not only make a difference in each patient's experience, but also connect directly to medical outcomes.

Similarly, when you have dinner at a restaurant and the service is great, you are left with the impression that the manager/owner of the restaurant wants customers to be treated well and has a focus on excellent customer service. If you experience poor service (especially by more than one person), you are left with the impression that the manager/owner of the restaurant doesn't really care.

Each time a staff member (receptionist, nurse, medical assistant, scheduler, billing specialist, etc.) interacts with patients in a cheerful, welcoming, and professional manner, the patients are more likely to feel that the doctor really cares about them. The more they feel the doctor cares about them, the more the patients trust the doctor and really listen to what the doctor is saying. The more the patients listen, the more likely they are to follow the doctor's advice—and the more likely it is that their medical outcomes will improve!

Improved medical outcomes

Patient is more likely to follow the treatment plan

Patient really listens to what the doctor is saying

Patient feels the doctor and team really care about them

Patient is interacted with in a cheerful and professional manner

Patient care and satisfaction require more than an excellent physician. As we stated in chapter 1, physicians cannot do what they do without an entire team. Go out of your way to regularly find examples of how each staff member plays a vital role in providing excellent care for each of your patients. To have a cohesive team, members must understand the important role they each play in the overall purpose.

This is well illustrated by the fable of the three bricklayers. As the story goes, three bricklayers are building a cathedral. A stranger to the city walks by and asks what they're doing. The first grimly replies, "What does it look like? I am laying bricks." The second responds, "I am feeding my wife and my children." The third says, "I am building the cathedral where people will be saved for all eternity."

Answering the phones, checking people in, drawing blood, and submitting claims for services rendered may not be considered as glamorous or exciting as preventing, diagnosing, and treating diseases, but how well these tasks are performed is ultimately as important to your practice as respiration, digestion, and circulation are for our bodies. Helping your staff continually see their roles as vital and appreciated is one of the keys to providing great leadership. It pays to regularly find examples of each staff member's contributions to your patients.

2. *People are free to speak up with their ideas, suggestions, and concerns. They know their voices matter.*

Let's imagine you have a young receptionist who thinks of a more efficient, less expensive way to handle patient check-ins. In your office, what is the likelihood that the receptionist will be successful in sharing the idea and being heard, that a pilot program will be run with multiple iterations, that the process will be refined and honed, and that the patients will receive more efficient, effective care (plus, by the way, that the practice will become more profitable)?

If this seems unlikely to happen in your practice, then you have an opportunity to discover a new level of medical leadership. How do you create a receptive, constructive process for this kind of improvement to occur within your practice? First, your employees must feel they can share their ideas and concerns without criticism or retribution.

Begin by creating and managing a forum for communication, such as daily team meetings, weekly staff meetings, or quarterly retreats. Think back on meetings that were valuable to you. What did they have in common? While working with a group of over 180 practices, we found some key concepts to consider:

- Create a regular schedule of meetings to ask your staff for input.

- Begin your meetings by reading or referring to the mission/vision statement.

- Remind everyone of the ground rules. Ask for mutual respect and open-mindedness, state the intention and the time allotted for the meeting, and initiate the discussion. During every meeting, model the behavior you desire from the staff so others understand what this looks like in action.

- Focus the discussions on what's working and what's not working. Highlight what is working and address what's not working from a place of partnership. Give people the benefit of the doubt rather than assigning blame. Be ready to redirect the conversation back to *what's* not working if the focus becomes *who's* not working.

  * Ask for group members' points of view on key proposals, and let them know where you are in your decision-making process.

  * Brainstorm (a conversation for possibility): Use a brainstorming format to collect ideas for solutions to what's not working. You will not only gather a wealth of information, you will also strengthen the collaboration within your team.

  * Narrow the possibilities (a conversation for opportunity): narrow down your list of possibilities to the ones that might be actionable in the near future.

> * Choose which solution to adopt (a conversation for action): identify and make a plan to adopt and institute a solution.

- Be approachable during the meeting as well as outside the meeting. When people ask you questions or share concerns, make sure your demeanor and verbal response convey your appreciation that they care and are engaged enough in their jobs to want to increase their knowledge and make things even better. Ask for their input on possible solutions, but don't give the impression that they alone must find a solution because that trains people to stop speaking up.

- Throughout the process, give them information and keep them updated.

- *Never* forget to acknowledge people for both their attitudes and their contributions.

· ·

Common Leadership Mistake

Not having regular team or staff meetings and thinking that meetings are merely about informing the staff rather than building a team

· ·

3. *People's skills, talents, and knowledge are used and make a difference.*

Fully use your staff. Honor people's contributions by using their skills, talents, and knowledge to the best possible extent. This is not only a benefit for the practice; it is a huge benefit for each individual. It is the role of leaders to bring out the best in their staff. Is it possible that despite good intentions, you've been accidentally diminishing the people on your team?

> *Some bosses stifle their employees, and some make them shine. Which kind are you? There are many ways to stifle the creativity and smarts of your team, just as there are lots of ways to get the most out of people.*
>
> —Liz Wiseman and Greg McKeown, *Multipliers*[2]

We have found that staff members are often not fully used or encouraged to be leaders. When individuals in a practice provide leadership, enthusiastic direction, and creative ideas, they begin to gel as a cohesive and dynamic team. In one of your staff meetings, inquire about the knowledge and talents that are being underused. You can say, "I know each of you contributes a lot to the operation of our practice. Do you sometimes think you have more to offer to help our patients and our practice? I'm not suggesting that you put in more time; I wonder if you have ideas for how we can make even better use of your talents and knowledge."

---

2   Liz Wiseman and Greg McKeown, *Multipliers: How the Best Leaders Make Everyone Smarter* (New York: HarperCollins, 2010). We recommend the book. It will give you additional insight into how to bring out the best in your staff.

4. People know that if something isn't working, it will be addressed in a respectful and professional manner so they can make corrections.

....

Common Leadership Mistake

Either avoiding uncomfortable conversations until you overreact or letting the issue go unaddressed at a high cost to your practice

....

Having the tools of *listening for* and being a *learner* allows you to begin the conversation in a responsive rather than a reactive way. These distinctions, which we fully outlined in chapter 2, completely shift conversations about what's not working and greatly increase the potential gains. Here are some more suggestions for creating respectful and professional discussions:

- If something isn't working, determine whether it needs to be attended to or accepted and let go. If it needs to be attended to, waiting only allows it to build further and to let unproductive behaviors become more deeply entrenched, usually compounding the emotional drama of the situation. (See chapter 9 for suggestions on an effective performance-improvement plan.)

- Use the five-to-one rule—five compliments (must be authentic compliments) to one piece of constructive input. People process compliments differently than they process constructive input or criticism. Studies have shown that when we hear positive comments instead of negative ones, we are much more likely to stay fully engaged. Focus on people's strengths—highlight and fully use those!

- Minimize gossip. Make a pledge that you and your team will not indulge in gossip. Productivity will increase and people will feel respected. We all have a tendency to talk about others. Our definition of gossip is talking critically about someone who is not present or giving information about a person that is not appropriate or necessary.

    One rule of thumb is to ask whether you would say the same thing in the same tone if the person were standing right there and if you were speaking from your commitment to empower people. If the answer is no, don't say it. It's also important to be clear that it takes a speaker as well as a listener for gossip to occur. Many times people think that if they haven't said anything negative, then they weren't gossiping. This is not true. If no one listened, there would be no gossip.

5. People feel supported and empowered by their colleagues as well as their supervisors.

When employees are left to guess what their supervisor and others in the office think of them, they may fill in the blanks with inaccurate or misguided perceptions. On the other hand, continually providing coaching and feedback may be interpreted as criticism, or that the employee is not doing well, when it is not meant that way at all. Mastering when to provide feedback and when to let others do their work takes sensitivity and practice. Here are some ideas for consideration.

- Coaching is one of the special opportunities leaders have to contribute to their staff and to empower and support them in reaching the next level. However, *only provide coaching and input when the other person requests it or is receptive.* This is a different category than making a request or discussing job duties, policies, etc. (which will be covered in chapter 6). If you have an idea you think will positively affect someone, yet the person hasn't asked for your input or suggestions, you can say, "I have a suggestion that I think will make a difference for you. Are you open or interested?" If the person says yes, then great—proceed. If not, say you respect that and the person is welcome to ask you about your suggestion in the future.

- Encourage your staff to offer help to each other and to speak up and ask when they need help themselves. In the culture of your practice, model the attitude that this is a sign of strength rather than weakness.

- Verify that each employee receives an annual review with feedback on all areas of strength as well as areas for improvement. Some practices find having a midyear review provides additional structure and lets employees know where they stand. Employee reviews are a formal opportunity to acknowledge your staff's contributions. When concerns are dealt with as they occur, surprises will be minimized at the annual or midyear review. (See chapter 9 for additional information about employee reviews.)

6. *People are recognized and appreciated for their work.*

....

Common Leadership Mistake
Only acknowledging people for significant accomplishments

....

The power of acknowledgment and appreciation is often underestimated. This is actually a gift for both the person giving the acknowledgment as well as the person receiving it. Recall a time when you authentically acknowledged another person. Did you feel like you became more closely connected to them? Did you feel that you made a difference by speaking your acknowledgment rather than merely thinking it? And now recall a time when a patient sincerely acknowledged you for your impact in their life. Did it make a difference that they told you rather than merely thinking it? Encourage your staff to acknowledge one another and to be gracious when receiving a compliment. When acknowledgment and appreciation are authentic and regular parts of the culture of an organization, it has a seemingly magical effect.

Remind everyone regularly of the specific and overall contributions they make. Tie this to the primary purpose of your practice—improved medical outcomes! It makes perfect sense that when your staff members feel taken care of, they are much more likely to take great care of your patients.

Practice

1. Review your Be, Do, Have list.

2. Continue to *listen for*, be a *learner*, and make your mission/vision statement a working document for your practice.

3. If you don't yet have regular staff meetings, get input from everyone about the least disruptive time and put it on the schedule.

4. Set and follow a meeting agenda and timeline. There are many good formats you can follow. Make sure to do the following in your meetings:

    • Read or reference your mission/vision statement.

    • Thank everyone for all they do (at the beginning of the meeting and again at the end).

    • Ask for input and ideas for taking the practice to the next level, resolving items that are not working, and highlighting areas that are working.

    • Give team members updates on new policies or plans.

    • Share what's coming up so the group is included in the bigger picture. This is a key opportunity for you to provide inspiration and a vision for what your practice is really all about.

5. During one of your staff meetings, make gossip a topic of discussion. Do not place blame or let it turn into a conversation about who gossips. Start by acknowledging that everyone has been guilty of this (yourself included). Ask what people think the positive impact would be if gossip were cut to a minimum. To be realistic, we don't recommend setting a goal of zero gossip. Be clear that gossip is destructive to people's respect and motivation to play full-out. Ask people to raise their hands if they're willing to intentionally not engage in gossip.

6. If thanking and acknowledging people is not yet one of your strong suits, put a plan in place to intentionally add this to your interactions with your team members.

7. Assess your leadership style. Go to www.multipliersbook.com and take the survey at the bottom of the home page.

How to Get Things Done

Action Makes the Difference

Some people think the grass is greener on the other side of the fence. Actually, the grass is greener where it is watered.

Anonymous

> Bring clarity and precision to the conversations that increase coordinated action by your team and see results at a much quicker pace, with fewer mistakes and less drama along the way.

Have you ever found yourself speaking in generalizations or expressing wishful thinking? For example, have you ever said to your nurse, "We are continually running late. I wish we could figure out how to stay on time," or "The phones take too long to answer. I hear complaints about it all the time"? What happens with this kind of communication? Two weeks later, are things usually better or the same? If your practice is the way mine was, the only thing that's different in two weeks is your level of frustration and disappointment that things are not better.

In the 184 offices within the medical group we used to work with, we would often see providers voice concerns week after week without change. Finally one day, frustrated and disappointed, the provider would lose it and yell at the office staff or make disparaging or condescending remarks. Staff satisfaction and turnover would both get worse, and little or nothing would improve. Upon further investigation, we would often hear, "I told the nurse/receptionist/ practice manager again and again things had to improve. He never listened to me. I don't think he cared as much as I do about the practice. I had to do something!"

When you stop and think about this approach, is it really surprising it failed? Suppose you were in the ICU and said to the nurse, "I wish the patient's CO_2 level were lower," or "The patient's urine output over the past twenty-four hours has been too low. I really hate it when patients' renal function decreases." What would change? It goes without saying that unless you adjusted the ventilator settings or the fluid management on the orders, nothing would change. It is intuitive for us to write time-limited, specific, metric-based goals and to set up a system of checks and balances to make sure they occur in the ICU: "Administer 40 mg of furosemide IV x1 now. In two hours if the urine output is < 500 mLs, administer an additional 80 mg of IV furosemide. If < 500 mLs two hours after this dose, please contact me." Now things will improve, or you will be informed and the next steps can be taken.

So how do we reproduce this in our offices in a collaborative and successful manner? What if you met with the practice manger and asked her what her specific goals were in regard to wait times and answering the phone? You could be surprised and learn some metrics were already being collected, such as times from check-in to checkout, times from check-in to doctor signing in the chart, number of telephone rings before calls are answered, or telephone wait times. If this is not being done, you and the manager could decide on the best metrics and establish mutually agreeable goals. Then a request such as, "Will you monitor this for two weeks and schedule a meeting in three weeks to see what we've learned so we can decide on the next steps?" would make sense, and significant progress toward improvement would have begun.

At the next meeting, if the results confirm your suspicion that things are not going well, then a simple diagram can be drawn to identify delays or bottlenecks, and strategies to correct the delays can be agreed upon. Two weeks later, the metrics can be recalculated and improvement (or lack thereof) followed. Much like in the ICU, you identify key variables, take action, and monitor the results. Unlike in the ICU, this process can be much more collaborative, and at times the staff may be able to handle the process on their own with your encouragement and support.

The other discovery you will surely make in this process is that much as renal function is often significantly affected by cardiac output, the different functions of your office are also interrelated. If the nurse doesn't take the time to answer questions from the telephone staff, it prevents a timely response to the patient's questions, which increases the calls, bogs down the phones, results in redundant calls and requests, confuses the staff, and leads to multiple call-backs—sometimes with conflicting information—and so forth.

Perhaps the most common and dangerous assumption leaders make is that others don't care as much as the leader does and this is the source of the failure. Upon further examination, you will find that this is not the case at all, and attempting to solve problems with this perspective usually creates additional communication challenges and compounds the problems, increasing the likelihood of failure.

Solutions are found by having an open mind and a willingness to discover the challenges. It's essential to start with the assumption that staff members care as much as you do and are functioning as well as they can given the limitations of the system. *Listening for* their commitment and acknowledging their efforts is vital. In this process, you will often discover how hardworking and committed to success your team members are, frequently in ways you would never have thought of or appreciated if you had not slowed down enough to understand their efforts and work.

By changing your orientation from "what is wrong with the people" to "what isn't working at the office," you empower everyone to participate in finding solutions. And by breaking things down into manageable steps, you allow the team to appreciate your goals and productively engage in the process with you.

These small steps will overcome the practice's challenges one by one—and then the next weakest link or challenge will emerge. This iterative process of gradual improvement will ultimately result in many of your goals being met or exceeded. The key to bridging the gap between great ideas and great results is gradually and consistently staying in action to accomplish goals and empowering others to do the same.

Key Distinctions to Get Things Done

As we've said previously in this book, a physician cannot practice medicine in today's world without a team—one person cannot do everything that needs to be done. Therefore, coordinated action is required. As a leader, you have the opportunity to bring clarity and precision to this process. You will then see results at a much quicker pace, with fewer mistakes and less drama along the way.

Without realizing it, all of us at times gravitate toward avoiding responsibility and accountability. This is our egos wanting to avoid looking bad or being wrong if we don't succeed. The good news is that when we are reminded or remind ourselves to be *learners* and set our egos to the side, we become naturally willing to step up, take responsibility, and be accountable for our actions. This mindset shifts the process of following an action plan from drudgery or power struggles to excitement and fulfillment.

· ·

Common Leadership Mistake
Assuming others know what you want or what's expected of them

· ·

Distinction: Straight Talk

People sometimes use the phrase "straight talk" to justify being harsh and hurtful in their communication. They think if they call it straight talk, somehow that makes it OK. The reality is that the cost to the relationship is the same no matter what you call it.

Straight talk is neither harsh nor nice. We define it as direct and honest talk. It is fact based, commitment based, and action oriented. It is speaking to generate action toward a change in behavior rather than avoiding the real subject or talking around a topic. To be effective, it must be respectful, or it will fall into the harsh category and trigger resistance or suppression. If it is overly nice, it won't be taken seriously.

To bring clarity and precision to the process of moving your practice forward, make your new mantra "Who will do what by when?" At the end of every conversation, whether in the hallway, with a patient, or in a meeting, ask yourself, "Based on this conversation, is there action required?" If the answer is yes, clarify that everyone involved is clear on who will do what by when.

Here's a simple example: If you and your medical assistant have a conversation about how pleased you are a patient is feeling better, no action is required. If you have a conversation with your medical assistant about a patient you've seen for years who has not kept his last two appointments, then action is very likely required to make a difference. You could clarify who will call the patient to check in with him by a certain date. Most of the time, conversations or meetings have many moving parts and require several actions to achieve the desired result.

Distinction: Committed Listening and Speaking

Committed listening and speaking are designed to propel action. How you listen and speak can either motivate or impede action for yourself and others.

Committed speaking is clear, is precise, and calls forth action. *Nothing happens in any organization unless discussions result in action.*

Many times people are hesitant to make promises. They feel that making a promise will trap or box them in, and they try to avoid that feeling by being vague. They fear they might not succeed at fulfilling the promise, and they don't want to disappoint the other person or themselves or look bad. That fear is mostly a function of not understanding what integrity means in regard to promises.

Promise: A commitment to another person to fulfill specific conditions of satisfaction by a particular time.

Request: Asking another person to commit to fulfilling specific conditions by a particular time.

A request is not complete until a person has accepted the request verbally or in writing, thereby making a promise.

Productivity will increase when

1. the conditions of satisfaction are 100 percent clear to both people;

2. promises and requests are put in writing so an action will be triggered. (This can be done using an action grid that is regularly reviewed or entering items into a reminder system like Outlook's.)

Here are four possible effective responses to requests:

1. Accept the request and take on the task. This now constitutes a promise: "Yes, I will do A by our agreed-upon completion date."

2. Decline the request: "Unfortunately, I cannot do that." Unless people are free to decline a request or say no, they can't say yes with full authenticity.

3. Make a counteroffer: "I can't do A, but I could do B," or "I can do A by a different deadline."

4. Commit to commit later: "I will check my calendar, gather necessary information, and give you a yes or no by (a certain time)."

Recognizing that you and others always have these four options for responding to requests will foster authenticity in your relationships. This may seem subtle, but we suggest that thinking you are trapped or don't have a choice puts you in the victim role. Of course, as with every choice, there are consequences (positive or negative). For example, declining a request that is part of your job will certainly create consequences, including possible termination from the job.

Any response other than one of these leaves the conversation vague. Here are examples of common responses that actually impede productivity and effectiveness: "I'll try";

"I hope we can get it done by then"; "So, Monday is the deadline?"; "We should have it done soon"; etc.

Integrity—How to Revoke, Revise, Cancel, and Follow Up

Circumstances and situations sometimes change. It is unrealistic to think people will always fulfill every promise as originally made. When we continue to focus on strengthening our relationships and know these relationships are crucial to what we want to accomplish, it's natural to responsibly tend to our promises and requests.

Revoking or revising a promise does not make it a broken promise or indicate a lack of integrity. In fact, depending on how and when we revoke or revise our promises, doing so can mean we are operating at a high level of integrity.

Canceling a Request

Low or no cost to the relationship—As soon as possible, notify the people who will be affected that the request is no longer needed and is withdrawn. Thank them for being willing to take it on.

High cost—Fail to notify people until they've spent considerable time on the request, the agreed-upon completion date is close, or they've already fulfilled the promise (very high cost).

Revoking a Promise

Low or no cost to the relationship—As soon as you realize you will not be able to fulfill the promise, notify everyone who will be affected. Apologize for any inconvenience or problems created by this change. Take responsibility for your choice to revoke your promise, and don't blame anyone or anything.

High cost—Fail to notify everyone until it is close to the agreed-upon completion date. Don't apologize, take responsibility for this change, or consider how it affects others.

Requesting a ride to the airport is a good example of how this works. The longer someone waits to respond to your request, or the later the person revokes the promise to give you a ride, the greater your level of anxiety and the fewer your workable alternatives. An additional cost is the lost sense of reliability in the relationship—and the longer the delay in responding, the higher the cost. The way we communicate when it's necessary to either revoke or revise a promise is also important. If our communication is haphazard or overly dramatic, the cost to the relationship tends to be higher. The lesson here is to respond to requests and communicate the need to revoke promises as soon as possible.

Revising a Promise

Low or no cost to the relationship—Use this option only when truly necessary. Notify everyone who will be affected that you either need to revise the specifics of what you will do or the agreed-upon completion date. Be considerate of how this may inconvenience others, and have a conversation that reflects your commitment to the results and solutions that work for everyone involved.

High cost—Make frequent changes to what you agreed to do or the completion date.

Breaking a Promise

Low or no cost to the relationship—There is always at least some cost to our relationships when we fail to fulfill our promises and let the agreed-upon completion date go by without communicating responsibly.

High cost—Every time we let an agreed-upon completion date go by without fulfilling the promise or notifying others of a change, there is a high cost to the relationship. Even if the circumstances changed and it was appropriate not to fulfill the promise, our failure to acknowledge the change prior to the agreed-upon completion date leaves the clear impression that we are not reliable.

It significantly increases the productivity of your practice when you can depend on team members to do what they say they will do. If someone has made a promise and broken it, call and meet with her to discuss the broken promise right away (the sooner the better). Start by acknowledging her commitment to the organization's and her own success, and then point out that she did not fulfill her promise.

A discussion about what happened might generate a teachable moment. Remember to *listen for* this person's commitments behind and between any excuses he might offer for the broken promise. End the discussion by forgiving him, ideally after—but not contingent upon—an apology from him, and state your confidence in his future performance. Recurrent broken promises require that much more emphasis be placed on the consequences of such behavior.

Following Up on Promises Made to You

Low or no cost to the relationship—When someone has made a promise to do something that is vital, let her know in the original discussion that it is important to keep you informed, and set up a schedule for regular updates (daily or weekly). Also make it clear that from time to time you will check in with her to see if she wants or needs any guidance. That way, she will be less likely to feel surprised or micromanaged when you check in. Always include an acknowledgment of her time, effort, and accomplishments in your update discussions.

High cost—Approach the person's commitment with a hands-off mentality. Don't follow up at all or give him any acknowledgment along the way; conversely, micromanage by dictating every step of the process and being so involved that you might as well have done it yourself. This also has a high cost to the relationship, and it's a very inefficient use of people's time and talents.

. . . .

Common Leadership Mistake
Either being hands-off or micromanaging

. . . .

Request Chart

Effective Request	Ineffective Request
I request that you submit your completed weekly report to me by 5 p.m. this Friday. Do you accept my request?	Can you try to get your report to me as soon as possible? (No request made for the completed report—this is a request only to "try," plus it doesn't give a deadline.)
Will you please send me your completed weekly report by the end of the day Friday? (Not as formal as above, yet it's still a powerful request.)	I really would like for you to get the report to me by the end of the week. (No request was made—just a statement of what you would like.)
	It is really important that you get this report completed. (No request—just a statement regarding the importance.)

Promise Chart

Clarifying Questions	Effective Response	Ineffective Response
What details do you want in the report?	**Accept/Promise** Yes, I accept your request. Yes, I will do that. Yes, I will have the report to you on Friday. Yes, you can count on me for that.	I'll give it a try. (There's no commitment to completing it and no mention of when.)
Do you want the report to show all activity for the week or only the results?	**Counteroffer** I can commit to getting the report to you on Monday. Will that work? (This is a counteroffer; the requester now accepts or declines the counteroffer.)	I think I'll be able to do that. (Again, there's no commitment.)

Clarifying Questions	Effective Response	Ineffective Response
	Decline No, I decline your request. Unfortunately, it won't work for me to do that. No, I am not willing to do that. (Note that there may be minor or major consequences to declining certain requests.)	Yes (when you're not clear on the request and don't really know what is needed in a weekly report).
	Commit to commit later I think I can get the report to you on Friday. I'll check my calendar first, and I'll let you know one way or the other by noon today. (Then give a yes or no at that time.)	

. . . .

Common Leadership Mistake
Not effectively delegating tasks and projects

. . . .

Leadership is really about rallying people so they excel individually and as a team. It's necessary for team members to be operating at their highest level of knowledge, skill, and credentials. Therefore, delegating projects and tasks to the appropriate person in the most effective manner is crucial for the success of the leader and the team.

Effective delegation seems to be quite rare. We often see the hot-potato style, where a task is tossed to team members in hopes that they will take care of it. This is a recipe for frustration and often failure on everyone's part. The other mistake we often see falls into the category of micromanagement described above.

Ineffective delegation is very costly. It wastes time and money by causing confusion about who is doing what, duplicated efforts (more than one person doing the same tasks), and reduced productivity (due to the time required to resolve the upsets created or to replace employees who leave as a result of not being empowered in their jobs). There is also the cost of what wasn't but could have been accomplished had everything been delegated effectively.

Seven Steps for Effective Delegation

1. Define your intended results. Common mistake: not being clear about what you really want to happen or continuing to move the target.

2. Select an appropriate employee. Common mistake: immediately giving the task to someone close by rather than really considering who would be the best person on the team for this task.

3. Determine and communicate the level of delegation. Common mistake: telling someone this is his project but actually thinking that you'll still be the final decision maker, or wanting him to take the lead and being frustrated when he is waiting on your input. Be honest with him. Example: "Please give me several possible options and your top two recommendations. I will then make a final decision." Or, "Please complete the

task. Just let me know what you've done so I'm informed."

4. Clarify expectations and set parameters. Common mistake: having a certain process, budget, and so forth in mind but not letting the person know.

5. Give authority to match the level of responsibility. Common mistake: expecting others to move forward when they have not been given the authority to do so.

6. Provide background information. Common mistake: not sharing the whole picture. It is motivating and useful for an employee to know how this task or project fits in with the bigger picture.

7. Arrange for feedback during the process. Common mistake: not communicating expectations for the frequency and method of updates during the process. Example: "In addition to our weekly or monthly staff meetings, I would like you to send me an e-mail each Friday with an update on this project. If you have questions or would like to discuss the project more frequently, just let me know."

Action Grid

It is clear we cannot effectively manage and track all this in our heads. When you're serious about moving things forward, putting it in writing is a must. Find a system that works for you and your practice. There are many task-management tools available online to track the actions that have been agreed upon. Some of these systems are simple and straightforward; others are more complex and allow you to focus on short-term, long-term, and lifelong goals.

At a minimum, we recommend that you use a simple Excel spreadsheet that is kept up-to-date and reviewed at every staff meeting. This action grid would include these six columns:

- Area of Focus (*What's Next* or *What's Not Working* or *Area of Concern*)

- Specific Action Item

- By Whom

- By When

- Comments and Current Status (*On Track* or *Ahead* or *Behind*)

- Completion Date

Appoint an action grid manager to create a form or use the form we have provided, track and update each action—always including who and by when—and e-mail or hand deliver the revised form to everyone involved within two or three days after the meeting. This form will be a working document that is reviewed and updated at each meeting. (See the appendix for a simple action grid format.)

One way we would encourage you to use this chapter's information is to reduce wait times if your patient-satisfaction scores indicate long wait times are an issue. Extra wait time is not only upsetting for patients but is also a drain on the staff. One myth we hear is that there is no way around having wait times. We suggest that you can certainly minimize wait time. We've also found that the front desk staff, medical assistants, and people in the back of the office often see things and have ideas for reducing wait times that the physicians or practice managers may not have thought of. This could be a perfect project for effective delegation!

Practice

1. Review your Be, Do, Have list.

2. Continue to *listen for*, be a *learner*, and make your mission/vision statement a working document for your practice.

3. Continue to have regular staff meetings.

4. During one of your staff or team meetings, talk about implementing the ideas from this chapter in your practice. Ask whether your practice manager would be willing to be the action grid manager. Block out the necessary time in your schedule to successfully fulfill your promises. Lead by example—complete your promised actions on time. When necessary, revise or revoke promises in a responsible manner prior to the deadline. Remember, you set the pace for the success of this process.

5. Continue to go out of your way to acknowledge and show your appreciation for your staff. Encourage your staff to acknowledge each another as well.

Dealing with the Bumps in the Road

Misunderstandings, Irritations, Complaints, Etc.

When will we have an entire day with zero upsets? When we're six feet under.

Anonymous

> Over- or underreacting to upsets in your practice is costly. You lose enjoyment, time, and money, and it impacts patient care. Enjoy a new sense of freedom and increased productivity from effectively resolving upsets.

How many upsets have occurred in your office this week? This could include you getting upset with your staff, your patients, or other physicians; your patients getting upset with your staff, or even with you, about their circumstances; or your staff getting upset with each another, your patients, or you. You get the picture. Upsets—small, medium, or large—occur on a regular basis. It could be said that life is a never-ending parade of upsets.

Have you ever noticed that upsets seem to be contagious? When they are left unattended, they often multiply and spread to other people. Effective leadership includes using your influence to resolve upsets so team members can return their focus to providing great care for your patients.

If you have applied the distinctions and concepts in the first five chapters of this book, it's very likely you have already experienced a reduction in upsets at your practice. However, given that upsets are a natural part of being human and will always be a part of life, learning to be very skilled in dealing with and resolving them makes sense.

Here are some things we do unconsciously that actually add to the upsets in our lives:

1. We have the mindset that we shouldn't have upsets or that when we get everything just right, our lives will be free of upsets. The sooner we stop resisting our current reality and start embracing upsets as part of life, the sooner we can effectively deal with the upsets, learn from them, and move forward.

2. We have the mindset that life will be better when we are fully staffed, our patient volume is where we want it to be, our patients follow their treatment plans, and so on. It is fascinating how we wait for other people and/or circumstances to change so our lives will turn out the way we want. Of course, as covered in chapter 5, it is valid and appropriate

to make requests of others as we manage our daily affairs and create intentional changes in our lives. However, when we make changes reactively or wait passively for others to change, we abdicate our power and end up being victims in our own lives.

One way we regain our power is by reminding ourselves that every challenge presents an opportunity for growth and improvement personally and for the practice. Begin the process of effectively resolving upsets by asking yourself what role you played in a situation that didn't go well. Do this without self-blame or guilt. You are just looking for something you missed earlier. Then ask yourself, "What can I do going forward that will make a positive impact?"

. . . .

Common Leadership Mistake
Not addressing employee and patient upsets quickly and effectively and hoping the upsets will just go away

. . . .

Some of us have a strong tendency to avoid conflict. But when you step over something that needs to be addressed, the negative effect and cost can be very high. You may try to convince yourself that although you didn't have the greatest possible impact, at least you didn't cause any harm. Our assertion is that by not addressing issues in a timely manner in your practice, you are in fact having a negative impact.

Negative Consequences of Not Addressing Issues in a Timely Manner

1. You send the wrong message to others. They think that either you don't see the issue (and therefore have little awareness of what's going on), or that you see the issue but think it isn't worth addressing. People may even draw the conclusion that you are condoning the situation or that you just don't care.

2. You become a negative role model for your staff by allowing things to slide (plus you reinforce any personal tendency to be passive).

3. You abdicate your power and place yourself in the victim role.

4. You miss the opportunity to quickly identify areas for improvement and make valuable adjustments in the practice.

By the end of this chapter, you will have a wealth of knowledge about what causes upsets and, more importantly, how to emotionally and logistically resolve or complete an upset. These distinctions will be helpful when you are the one who is upset, as well as when you are supporting someone else who is upset.

Distinction: The Anatomy of an Upset

When you dissect an upset, you will discover that it is a function of one, two, or all three of the following elements:

- An unfulfilled expectation. We all have conscious expectations as well as expectations that we're not aware of. When these expectations are unfulfilled, it triggers an upset.

- A thwarted intention. We have specific goals and objectives. When our intentions are thwarted or blocked, it triggers an upset.

- Withheld communication. We have thoughts, ideas, and feelings that could make a difference or be valuable when expressed. When we withhold or suppress these communications, it triggers an upset.

Example: You're driving to the office when you hear the "thump, thump, thump" of a flat tire on your car. You safely pull to the side of the road. If you were driving to the office on a Saturday afternoon when the office was closed so you could catch up on some paperwork, or were heading to the office with just enough time to start a full schedule of patients, how would the level of your upset vary? And if you used to be chronically late and had recently started arriving on time, how upset would you be? Most of us have a background expectation that our cars will get us from point A to point B within an allotted period of time. When that doesn't happen, we have an unfulfilled expectation. If you had been actively working on being on time and were now going to be late, you'd also have a thwarted intention.

As a physician, you have expectations of the people who work with you—your medical assistant, nurse, fellow physicians, practice manager, and so on. Any time they don't meet your expectations, it will trigger some level of upset. If you don't resolve your upset in some way, you will be adding to the initial upset by withholding communication as well.

Example: You refer your patients to Dr. Smith when they

need a cardiac workup. His medical care is excellent, and you've been referring patients to him for years. However, he rarely communicates back to you without being contacted several times. You recently referred one of your new patients to Dr. Smith, and you have heard nothing from him. You're upset. Your expectation that Dr. Smith will keep you in the loop is once again unfulfilled. Thinking it must be obvious, you have never talked openly with Dr. Smith about your need to be kept informed, so there is a withheld communication on top of this recurring unmet expectation.

Example: You have encouraged your staff to think outside the box about ways to make the office run more smoothly in order to reduce patient wait times. Yet despite your staff trying different things, the situation has not improved. Not surprisingly, you're upset. Your intention to resolve the wait-time issue hasn't been successful, and you therefore have a thwarted intention.

Example: In healthcare, confrontation and conflict are often avoided, particularly with a supervisor or the doctors with whom you're working. By avoiding the momentary discomfort of sharing your concerns and instead stewing in them or judging those who aren't doing what you want, you compound the situation through withheld communication, which can lead to greater conflict at a later date.

When you feel your blood pressure rising, become short-tempered with your coworkers, or wish the day would end so you could just go home, it is worth taking a step back and asking yourself what the source of the growing upset is. By breaking it down and asking yourself which of the three components of an upset are occurring, you can begin to see the upsets for what they are rather than as a swirl of thoughts and emotions consuming you. The nonspecific, free-floating feelings that something is not right here or something is about to go very wrong, which lead to anxiety and distraction, are reduced. From our experience, the earlier we take the time to identify what is occurring and address it directly, the less likely it is that a blowup or a significant upset will occur. We move from being unclear, anxious, frustrated, and disempowered to being clear about the situation and engaged in the process of resolving it.

Mastery of Upsets

> *A happy life consists not in the absence, but in the mastery of hardships.*
>
> Helen Keller

When we leave upsets unresolved by trying to ignore them and hoping they will go away, minimizing them, or not cleaning them up with an apology and forgiveness, they build and generate resentment. Ultimately this can lead to a sense of resignation and powerlessness, which then stifles our passion and full commitment to making the biggest difference possible.

Distinction: Resolving an Upset

What we need is a set of tools for effectively resolving upsets. Begin by reminding yourself that people do not actually enjoy being upset. It's not fun! No one goes to bed at night and thinks, "I am so glad I lost my cool today." Or "I enjoy feeling really peaceful about the drama and turmoil I created and was part of today." Or "It's great that I withdrew in my relationships and now feel isolated." People do lie in bed at night and ruminate about the drama in their lives while looking for justifications for their reactions. Their thoughts may swirl with embarrassment, blame, and guilt. None of this equals enjoyment.

Therefore, the underlying element that will make the biggest difference in handling upsets masterfully is compassion—for ourselves when we are upset and for others when they are upset. This is not "feeling sorry for"—it is heartfelt caring for your and others' emotional pain or discomfort.

As soon as you recognize that you are experiencing some level of upset or that someone else is upset and you have the opportunity to offer support, we recommend that you take the following steps to reduce the chance you'll be reactive or ignore the situation.

Step 1:   Pause and take a deep breath.

Step 2:   Remind yourself that you have a choice. You can choose your mindset and decide to take actions that make matters better or worse.

Step 3:   Reignite your commitment to interact in a way that makes a positive impact. Envision yourself providing leadership and a human connection in the situation.

Step 4:   Determine when (which could be now or later), where (allowing for sufficient privacy), and how (possibly using tools from the list below) to best address the situation so everyone involved is empowered.

There are many different distinctions or tools that can be used to powerfully resolve an upset. We will present a few that you can practice to resolve your own upsets and to support your staff and patients in resolving theirs.

Tools for Resolving an Upset

1. **Use re-creation.** Truly get it from the other person's point of view. There is immense power in forming a rich connection with other people by putting ourselves in their shoes to the best of our ability. Rather than focusing on how you think someone *should* be dealing with a situation, respectfully look at how the situation occurs for him. This doesn't mean you're agreeing or disagreeing with his point of view. You're saying you respect his point of view. This is simple yet profound.

2. *Listen for* **other people.** Remind yourself that everyone is fundamentally committed to excellence. *Listen for* who the person is and for her commitments. See them as distinct from her actions. You can then relate to her powerfully and effectively address her actions (if appropriate) even when you're upset or she's upset. (Refer to chapter 1 to gain more insight into this distinction.)

3. **Look at what happened versus the interpretation.** Distinguish the facts from the interpretation of what happened. This seems simple, yet most of us do not accurately distinguish between what actually happened (facts) and our interpretations (opinions). We say things such as, "It's cold in the

office," when the accurate statement would be, "It feels cold to me in the office." The temperature is 73 degrees or whatever it is. One person may feel cold while another is quite comfortable.

Let's dissect this: Imagine I said, "Bob is rude. He's always interrupting me. He's so arrogant. He thinks what he has to say is more important than what I have to say." What part of that statement is fact? The answer is that there are no facts in that statement. Actually, everything in that statement is my interpretation. The fact about this situation, which is not communicated in that statement, is that from time to time Bob starts talking before I've finished my sentence.

All too often, we don't identify the facts, and we slide into believing our interpretations are facts. Unfortunately, we don't stop there. We collect evidence to validate our beliefs. And sometimes we move beyond indulging in false beliefs in our inner conversations (which has a high cost in and of itself) to talking with others and gossiping. This kind of office gossip is extremely costly to everyone on the team, not just the person being gossiped about.

As for my upset with Bob, what is the chance I can have a productive conversation with him while I believe my story about the situation? With my underlying belief that Bob is rude and arrogant, how might I come across if I were to request that he not interrupt me? What is the cost of just trying to avoid Bob? In most cases, both actions will reduce the productivity and cohesiveness of the team.

Separating fact from interpretation is not likely to immediately free me of my frustration with Bob, but it will allow me to look at the situation differently. I can now shift from thinking, "This is just the way Bob is" (which doesn't leave room for our relationship to be different) to powerfully listening *for* him and giving him the benefit of the doubt. Maybe Bob was raised in a large family where you never got to talk if you didn't interrupt. Maybe he has weak social skills and doesn't easily recognize the give-and-take of an effective conversation. Maybe Bob is very passionate about the topics we discuss and jumps in too soon. Or maybe Bob does think what he has to say is more important than what I have to say. (Who hasn't been guilty of that at some point in their lives?)

If I let go of my rigid conclusions about him, I have a much higher chance of handling my upset successfully. I can (1) accept that Bob interrupts me sometimes and that it's not worth talking it through with him (which means I don't hold it against him or gossip about him); (2) talk with him about the situation by saying, for example, "I know we are both committed to the success of this practice as well as to having the best relationship we can in order to support the practice. This is a little awkward for me, but I wanted to mention that it bothers me that you sometimes interrupt me. I'm sure I have interrupted you too. Anyway, it would be great for me if you would please let me finish when we're talking, and then I will fully listen to you too." This conversation could actually support the relationship in being authentic and productive.

4. **Apologize.** Apologize without giving excuses for what you did or said that didn't work for the other person. An authentic apology reaches into a relationship and provides an opening for emotionally completing an incident. We're focusing on what works and doesn't work in each individual relationship rather than what's right or wrong, how things should be, etc.

    *   An apology is distinct from "I'm sorry." It isn't a report on your feelings or a value statement. Letting someone know you feel sorry or feel bad can also be appropriate. When this is authentic, the vulnerability will be beneficial to the relationship. However, an apology goes further by expressing ownership and extends an offer of completion to the other person.

    *   When we deliver an apology that is inauthentic, we add additional distance in the relationship. One method of verifying the authenticity of your apology is to answer this question: do you have empathy for the other person, given the impact your actions had on him?

        Example: You arrive at the office in the morning with a poor attitude and are rude to your teammates. You make negative comments about everything they do that isn't exactly the way you want it to be, and you feel quite justified since you were on the phone for hours in the middle of the night dealing with admitting a critical patient to the ICU. However, given your treatment of your staff members, you owe them an apology. If you focus on your justification, you will either not deliver the apology or you will deliver an inauthentic and insincere apology. If you focus on your commitment to interacting with your staff in a way that's consistent with your mission/vision statement, as well as to treating staff members the way you want them to treat your patients even when they're having a rough time, you will deliver an authentic apology.

5. **Forgive.** Forgive yourself and others. This provides direct access to freedom. We all have the ability to forgive anyone for anything at any time. When we create forgiveness, it allows us to let go of resentment and guilt. To the degree that we are resentful and/or experiencing guilt, our vitality is diminished—which means our ability to contribute to others is also diminished.

Forgiveness can be thought of as a muscle that for many of us is weak and can be strengthened over time as we practice forgiving ourselves and others. Forgiveness is not condoning or saying the behavior in question is all right. Maybe what the other person did or didn't do was not all right and in fact damaged the relationship. Maybe what the other person did or didn't do caused severe problems. It's still possible to forgive. Forgiveness is not bound by the severity of the deed.

Example: You didn't return a call from the consulting doctor regarding your patient. You caused a time delay and an upset for everyone involved. Of course, you have your excuses. You may want to use those excuses and stick to your story. However, acknowledging in a professional manner that you dropped the ball and then apologizing for your mistake will go a long way toward resolving the upset. As a final step, forgiving yourself will be immensely powerful in allowing you to move forward without guilt or justification.

Example: You requested that your schedule be booked a particular way for new-patient appointments. You are midway through your day when you discover a new patient was scheduled without the length of time you requested. You may now feel resentful toward your staff, have a defeated mindset about the schedule for the day, and even start stewing about who needs to be fired. However, now is the time to let go of your anger and forgive your staff for the mistake, knowing you will deal with it later. This allows you to have peace of mind as you move through the day and to take great care of your patients. Without anger and resentment, you will be thinking clearly when you meet with your practice manager later to correct the problem. You can take appropriate action based on what will work best for your practice rather than being driven by anger.

Resentment is like drinking poison and waiting for the other person to die.

Japanese Proverb

6. **Replace irritation with insight.** What if someone called you a giant, alien, grass-eating monster? How irritated would you be? Most likely you would be surprised or amused but not irritated—it's too outlandish a statement, and you wouldn't take it seriously. So what does irritate you and why? Being aware of what our buttons are allows us to be responsible for our sensitive areas. This makes us less likely to blame others for emotions we're experiencing. Gaining insight into your buttons may be the next step to becoming really comfortable in your life. When you become tense, be aware of your body, your thoughts, and your emotions. What are your thoughts when you want to speak over or interrupt someone? What are you concerned the person may be thinking about you? What are the situations that trigger your insecurities? (We all have them.) These insights can have a positive impact by helping you become less reactive.

7. **Match emotion with emotion—and then match logic with logic.** How we respond emotionally to another person when they are upset either helps dissipate the upset or adds to it like gasoline on a fire. Think of a time when you were upset and told someone about the situation. If the person tried to tell you why you shouldn't be upset, or responded using only logic and didn't sincerely acknowledge your emotions, your upset feelings would most likely have increased.

Example: If your patient is upset about something, the most effective way you can respond is with compassion that's at the same level as the upset. If he's angry about the length of time he spent in the waiting room before seeing his doctor, and his frustration is at a level six on a scale of one to ten, then what's likely to make him feel heard and respected is to have compassion for him at a level six. Compassion at a level nine or ten will come across as exaggerated and insincere. Compassion at a level two or three will come across as uncaring. When the level of his emotions has begun to lessen and he shifts from focusing on the emotional element of the upset to the logical element, you can also address the logical element. But starting the conversation with the logical statement that your office has been extremely busy and is running behind will most likely leave him feeling not cared about. The information might be valid, yet not first having compassion for his emotions will reduce the experience of human connection.

8. **Take action.** Take action that's consistent with your commitment. Clean up what didn't work by correcting the situation and/or ensuring that it doesn't happen again. It is extremely powerful and effective to shift your mindset, apologize, and forgive other people. However, this is not enough in certain situations. We are all familiar with the phrase "Action speaks louder than words." In some situations, doing what it takes to follow

through with appropriate action will make the biggest difference.

Example: You have been chronically late getting to the office in the morning. You know it is problematic for everyone involved, but you have been justifying it; at some level you even believed that this was just how it was for you. Now you are ready to effectively deal with the upset you've been causing in your office. What's next?

Apologizing and taking responsibility is only the first step. For some people, apologizing for being late is merely a part of the pattern, and over time it diminishes the power of the apology. What is required to resolve this particular issue is to actually be on time. Therefore, the second step is taking whatever actions are necessary to get you there on time.

Here are some actions you could take:

* Make a verbal promise to yourself to be on time starting tomorrow, and share your commitment with your practice manager or another appropriate person.

* Review your schedule and be realistic about your sleep requirements, the time needed for your morning ritual, your commute time, etc.

* Make whatever changes are necessary to get to the office with time to spare. (This cushion of time is crucial, especially when forming a new habit).

* Track your success in being on time for two or three months to actually stabilize the new pattern.

* Set your ego aside so you don't fall back into defending your previous lateness.

* Acknowledge the benefit that you being on time has for yourself, your staff, and your patients.

Becoming upset or having those around us become upset is a natural part of life. Being an effective leader requires quickly and gracefully moving from the state of upset to the state of clarity in order to shift the focus back to our patients and the work at hand. In this chapter, we have offered tools and distinctions that can help you in this endeavor.

The freedom that comes from resolving the swirl of conflict or confusion can make you feel as if a weight has been lifted off your shoulders; you feel lighter and experience more energy. From a physiological perspective, the reduction of stress hormones facilitates a calm, focused, relaxed flow, as opposed to the charged, adrenaline-filled, ready-for-battle state that accompanies conflict.

Having someone you can trust—who has your best interests and the best interests of the practice at heart—as your coach or sounding board can be invaluable when you are committed to growing and taking your practice to the next level. In your discussions with that person, focus on the resolution of upsets instead of having typical commiserating conversations.

The more you use and practice these tools, the more quickly and effectively you will be able to move through upsets. With mastery of these skills, your life will flow more easily and spontaneously, allowing you to enjoy and flourish in your practice.

Additionally, sharing these tools with your staff will allow the people around you to start to move through upsets more effectively as well, reducing the feeling that you have to do it all yourself. This is a key part of the transition from cowboy leadership to team-based leadership. It takes time and is worth every minute!

Practice

1. Continue to *listen for*, be a *learner*, and make your mission/vision statement a working document for your practice.

2. Identify one upset in your practice that you have been avoiding. Which of the tools listed above could you use to resolve this upset? Ask your practice manager, nurse, or another coworker to read this chapter and partner with you in using these tools to resolve the upset.

3. When that upset is complete, use the momentum to take on a second upset in the practice, strengthening your upset-resolution muscle.

4. Acknowledge your staff each time an upset is effectively resolved. You will be highlighting and reinforcing this important element of teamwork.

5. Have either the physician or practice manager connect by e-mail or telephone with each patient who has a complaint within forty-eight hours of receiving the complaint. Powerfully address their concern utilizing the appropriate tools listed above with a commitment to resolve the upset.

Embracing Change

It is not the strongest of the species that survive, nor the most intelligent that survives. It is the one that is the most adaptable to change.

Charles Darwin

Learn how you can move beyond the natural tendency of resisting change to powerfully creating what's next.

Can you possibly count the number of changes that have been made in healthcare or your practice in the past three years? Responding to the Affordable Care Act and ICD-10, transitioning to EMR, and moving to population-based care are just a few at this writing. Have you made comments about the changes being unnecessary or problematic? How much time has your staff spent grumbling about the changes being implemented in your office? As we all know, the only thing that is constant is change itself, yet we often find ourselves resisting and wishing things didn't change.

What is actually occurring when we resist change? The beginning point of change is that something is ending or will end. It is completely natural for us to feel some loss and uncertainty at the beginning of a change in any area of our lives. When we experience uncertainty, our inner thoughts probably sound something like this:

- "How is this going to affect me or our practice?"

- "How big of an ordeal is this going to be?"

- "Will this end up being a good thing in the long run?"

- "How much work and money is this going to take?"

We then frequently move from uncertainty to skepticism:

- "This will never work."

- "Whose idea was this, anyway?"

- "I can't believe we have to do this."

- "The way we used to do it was better."

If you study uncertainty and skepticism, you will find uncertainty is a healthy early part of change and skepticism is the slide into being a victim. Skepticism ends up being destructive and paralyzing when we stay in it for long. Moving from skepticism to exploration is the magical moment in effectively dealing with change.

Moving to exploration sounds like this:

- "How can we make this work?"

- "How can we implement this so it's seamless for our patients?"

- "What can I do to ensure this makes the biggest difference possible for everyone involved?"

- "I liked the old way, but who knows, maybe this is actually going to be better in the long run."

- "I'm open-minded. I'll make this work."

From exploration we begin to experience a new commitment to making the change work and effectively moving forward.

Be aware that when you are the one making the decisions or you have direct influence with the decision makers, skepticism is equally toxic. It will never empower people or foster success. If your instinct is that the plan needs to be reconsidered or altered, you will have a positive impact by shifting into exploration:

- "I have concerns about the new plan being successful. I will schedule a discussion with the others involved to take another look and further explore our options."

- "I'm not confident the decision I made is best for the practice. I will meet with the appropriate people to review the situation anew and explore our options."

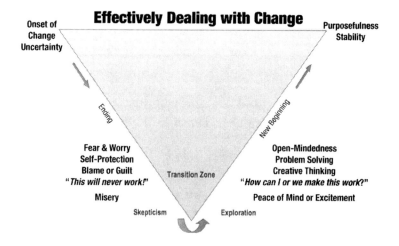

Maintaining Effectiveness during Times of Change

You can maintain your effectiveness even during times of change by not becoming stuck in skepticism. We assert that any misery we experience in new situations is a result of staying in the skepticism mode. We make ourselves miserable by indulging in negative thoughts. It really isn't the new policy, the new equipment, or the new fee schedule that makes us miserable.

Of course, when you have a sudden or major life change, what will help initially is to have compassion for yourself. Then move from the skepticism to exploration mode as quickly as possible. Sometimes this is difficult to grasp. However, since any misery we experience is a function of our thoughts, the good news is that we can always shift into empowering thoughts!

....

Common Leadership Mistake
Complaining about changes while expecting others to fully apply themselves and do their best to implement the changes

....

Adaptability—Dealing with Change

When you're finished changing, you're finished.

Ben Franklin

Shifting from the Victim Mindset to the Creator Mindset

Most people would say they don't have a victim mindset and that when they see someone being a victim, it is very unattractive, not to mention unproductive. If most people think they're not being victims, but they see plenty of people who are, then guess what? Most of us have a blind spot and don't recognize when we ourselves are being victims.

Let's be clear that whenever we are being victims, we have abdicated our power. If you look back at our description of the thoughts we have when we're skeptical, you'll see that being a victim is a part of that. Any time we feel trapped or stuck, we are being victims. Whenever we act as though we don't have a choice, we're being victims. We assert that life is a series of choices in every waking moment (although most of our choices are made at an unconscious level), and times of change always present the risk of slipping into the victim role.

There are many books that discuss the human phenomenon of being a victim. David Emerald addresses this mindset head-on in his book *The Empowerment Dynamic™*, as well as in his book *TED* for Diabetes*, cowritten by Scott Conard, MD (the coauthor of this book). These books can help you identify when you're being a victim and teach you how to shift to being a creator in the situation—even when you're not the one making the new policies.

*The Empowerment Dynamic™
By David Emerald[1]

Dreaded Drama Triangle ⟶ The Empowerment Dynamic
DDT   TED

Rescuer   Persecutor   Creator

Victim   Challenger   Coach

Empower Yourself
Identify the role you're playing in any given situation!

---

1   David Emerald, *The Power of TED* (*The Empowerment Dynamic™)* (Bainbridge Island: Polaris, 2006); David Emerald and Scott Conard, MD, *TED* (*The Empowerment Dynamic™) For Diabetes: A Health Empowerment Story* (Bainbridge Island: Polaris, 2012).

Victim: Do you have a sense of being powerless? Have you experienced some loss or thwarted desire or aspiration? Do you feel your happiness, sense of freedom, or success is dependent on someone or something else?

Persecutor: The persecutor may be you, another person, a condition (such as a health condition), or a circumstance. What is the cause of the victim's perceived powerlessness?

Rescuer: Who or what helps the victim relieve the "pain" of victimhood? The rescuer can be a person or an activity. The rescuing activity (such as an obsession or addiction) helps the victim numb out. The rescuing person reinforces (despite any helpful intentions) the victim's "poor me" attitude by adopting the "poor you" attitude, which increases the victim's sense of powerlessness. This renders the victim dependent upon the rescuer for a sense of safety.

Example: When people are told for the first time, "You have diabetes," it is not uncommon for them to be upset and feel like victims. What is the persecutor? Diabetes. What is needed? A rescuer from the disease. At this moment, it may be the doctor who offers the pill and education to manage the diabetes. The triangle is complete. For the first three months, things improve—the HgbA1c goes from 10.6 to 8.0, and the patient feels better. Three months later, the blood work comes back, and the A1c is now 9.2. The patient admits to slipping on the diet, exercising less, and missing a few doses of the medication. The doctor says, "Well, what do you expect? If you don't eat properly and exercise, your diabetes will get worse." Now the triangle shifts! The persecutor just changed from diabetes to the doctor who has seemingly attacked instead of rescuing the patient.

In this example, let's say the patient becomes upset, turns to the doctor, and loudly says, "You said I was doing better and that things would continue to improve. You misled me." Surprised, the doctor might respond, "Don't get upset with me. I can give you advice, but you have to follow it." Now the doctor is the victim, the patient the persecutor, and the nurse needs to come rescue the doctor from this long visit. This is the swirl of Dreaded Drama Triangle.™ Whenever a person doesn't fully accept responsibility or fails to work with and support the other person involved, this critical, defensive way of addressing problems becomes quite common, although costly.

By contrast, suppose the patient views the world through the lens of TED*. Instead of being the victim of a disease, the patient is the creator of her life. She would, after the initial shock or disappointment, see she has complete control over how she responds to the situation. Diabetes is then the challenger, and the patient is looking for a person who has more knowledge or experience (a coach) to help her become more capable of overcoming the challenge. To understand this more completely, let's further define the roles.

Creator: A creator greatly increases his ability to choose a response to life circumstances, even in the harshest of situations, rather than merely reacting to them. Do you cultivate your capacity to create outcomes by adopting a creator orientation? Do you intentionally nurture relationships that are empowering and harness dynamic tension (e.g., creator/challenger/coach)? Creators seek and form relationships with other creators to support and be supported through the other two roles that make up TED*.

Challenger: A challenger may be you, another person,

a condition (such as a health condition), or a circumstance. Are you a catalyst for change, learning, and growth for a creator? A challenger as a person is open-minded, conscious, and constructive, especially when in a relationship with another creator. Creators are able to embrace the experience of being challenged as a call to action, learning, and growth.

Coach: Do you view others as being creative and resourceful? Coaches see people they relate to as creators in their own right and seek to support them in the process of creating outcomes. A coach does this by asking questions that help clarify envisioned outcomes, current realities, and possible steps to move forward. A coach encourages creators to dream and discern the pathways for manifesting their visions.

Making Shift Happen

We have the opportunity to catch ourselves participating in the Dreaded Drama Triangle™ and to then shift to *The Empowerment Dynamic™ on a moment-to-moment basis throughout our lives. The shift from victim to creator takes place when we focus on what we want rather than what we don't want, reconnect to our dreams and desires, move from reaction to choice in our responses to life experiences, and take the stand that we can turn any circumstance into an asset in our lives. This allows us to make the transformation from protecting our egos to supporting empowerment in our relationships.

Human beings' default nature is to revert to what we have done in the past, so be alert for falling back into your old ways of coping with change and feeling like a victim. Make the shift from victim to resolver of upsets, and regain the momentum of your productive and empowered life.

Authenticity

All of this provides the opportunity to be honest with ourselves and to be authentic. Being "authentic," as we are using the term, means the degree to which you are true to your own spirit or character despite external pressures. It's when you lack pretense and let go of your attachment to looking good and keeping up appearances. This allows you to speak with honesty and vulnerability and keep your focus on contribution.

Being authentic also includes being willing to acknowledge when you slip into being a victim and to not pretend, for any reason, that you are always in the creator mode. We all know this is impossible. So be real, admit it when you slide back, and then again shift into the creator mode. This is not only liberating, it is also necessary for building a powerful, high-functioning practice.

Another benefit of modeling TED* as you lead the practice is that it encourages others to live their lives the same way—not perfectly, but always ready to shift to being a creator whenever they fall back into the victim mindset. The freedom to be yourself and not have to maintain an air of perfection is a gift to yourself and to those with whom you work. It is the leader's authentic passion and clarity for what's possible that allows empowering change to move the practice forward.

Practice

1. Continue to *listen for*, be a *learner*, and make your mission/vision statement a working document for your practice.

2. Identify one recent change in your practice that you moved through quickly and with relative ease. As you reflect on that experience, notice whether you spent a shorter amount of time in the skepticism mode and more time in the exploration mode.

3. Think of a current change happening in your practice, and intentionally shift your inner conversation from skepticism to exploration. Catch yourself when you revert to skepticism, and shift again.

Physician Leadership

If your actions inspire others to dream more, learn more, do more, and become more, you are a leader.

Unknown

> Gain a new level of clarity so that your strengths as a physician are used to make the biggest difference possible for the success of your practice.

Chapters 1 through 7 have provided information for physicians and everyone else who is part of a medical team. We hope you have read the first seven chapters of this book and have begun to apply many of the distinctions and recommendations to transform your practice. Chapter 8 is dedicated directly to the challenges that leadership brings for physicians. In this chapter we would like to take the opportunity to give you some additional information that pertains uniquely to the physician's leadership role in the practice.

Thinking about Your Practice

As a physician, what do you really want to do with your medical knowledge? Of course, you want your knowledge to be used to make a difference and help people. You also want your knowledge to support a successful practice and business. For that to happen, we believe it is crucial to have clarity about your role and the most effective way you can participate in the practice.

When you think about your practice, what do you consider to be your personal areas of strength—the areas where you absolutely knock it out of the ballpark? What are your personal weak spots—those areas where you are often frustrated or don't achieve the level of success to which you aspire? What would happen if you found ways to participate in your practice that strengthened your weak spots or kept them from interfering with the successful operation of the practice? How would your life and your practice be different? How could this improve results and reduce your stress level?

. . . .

Common Leadership Mistake
Confusing being an outstanding clinician with being an outstanding leader, manager, or teammate

. . . .

Some physicians are caught in a cycle of trying to do everything. Society holds doctors in high esteem, and many, if not most, doctors go on to assume that being intelligent and well trained in some select category of knowledge extends to many other aspects of life: business, management, money, relationships, and so forth. Though this collectively translates as an unrealistic expectation, it is a common one.

This puts doctors in a difficult spot. The role we are asked to play—being confident and secure in our knowledge and helping people make important and difficult decisions that have lifesaving or deadly consequences—comes with being a doctor. Patients want compassionate, skilled professionals with great maturity and knowledge guiding them in their battles with disease and disability. They don't want doctors who are well trained but have ineffective communication, management, leadership, social, emotional, or business skills.

For hospital administrators and staff members, doctors are important on multiple levels. Their vital medical role is magnified by the fact that doctors are the referral source for the hospitals' patients, and the orders doctors write determine how much revenue the hospital will receive. For doctors, the more patients are cared for, the more successful they are, and the more money and esteem they receive. It is a very effective positive-feedback loop.

What eventually comes of this is that some if not many of us actually start to believe our own PR. The way we think of ourselves evolves from "I am a really well-trained, hardworking, intelligent, motivated clinician with expertise in (fill in your specialty), and I have the opportunity to serve a group of people who need my expertise," to "I am really important, and my opinion about almost everything is correct." This false belief, the medical definition for a delusion, begins early in our career and requires unlearning.

Our culture's lofty and often-unrealistic expectations of doctors have run their course. Our changing healthcare system is requiring that physicians be highly scrutinized and measured clinicians as well as business leaders. Transparency and competition are increasing. Mistakes, omissions, excessive care, redundant care, excess costs, and quality ratings are increasingly being revealed to the public. Evidence-based medicine has led to numerous standards by which we are judged. Metrics like a practice's "gaps in care"—the difference between what has been done and what is recommended—are appearing on websites and in doctor directories.

At this time even the best practices are only scoring in the seventieth percentile. On average, in 2009 Americans received 70 percent of indicated healthcare services and failed to receive 30 percent of the care they needed to treat or prevent particular medical conditions. The gap between best possible care and what is routinely delivered remains substantial across the nation.[1] If these scores were grades in school, most if not all doctors in the United States would be failing some or all of their classes.

The public is increasingly unwilling to continue with this complex, expensive, and difficult-to-use system. Growing criticism is being aimed at modern medicine. Articles such as "U.S. Ranks Last among Seven Countries on Health System Performance Based on Measures of Quality, Efficiency, Access, Equity, and Healthy Lives"[2]

---

1 Agency for Healthcare Research and Quality, June 2013, http://www.ahrq.gov/research/findings/nhqrdr/nhqr12/highlights.html. Sponsored by AHRQ, Version 1.

2 The Commonwealth Fund, "U.S. Ranks Last Among Seven Countries on Health System Performance Based on Measures

commonly appear in the *New York Times* and other leading news outlets.

In response, policy and medical societies are encouraging doctors to change their thinking and begin to practice in a different way. Both the system and the care we provide are being deemed unacceptable. This is generating resistance and resentment among physicians. As Dr. Bruce Spivey and Dr. Walter McDonald reported in *The Measurement of Healthcare Performance*, "Some pushback by individual physicians is inevitable given ambivalence about the process and even paranoia about the external pressures which have been created in this movement. This combined with uncertainty about the process and concern about being evaluated does lead to some resistance."

So how will you respond to these challenges? Will defending yourself make a difference? Or will you take a more proactive approach to the changes?

Reframing the Practice

What if each of us clarified what our real areas of expertise are and are not? This is an opportunity to be honest with yourself that you are not an expert in all areas of life; that is an impossibility. In what areas are you experiencing frustration and/or receiving input from others that things are not working? Do you have challenges in the areas of management, business, emotional intelligence, balancing

---

of Quality, Efficiency, Access, Equity, and Healthy Lives," the Commonwealth Fund, June 23, 2010, http://www.common-wealthfund.org/News/News-Releases/2010/Jun/US-Ranks-Last-Among-Seven-Countries.aspx.

professional and personal time, etc.? You can shift from thinking, "I should know this," to realizing, "This is not yet an area of strength for me and might never be. I have not invested nearly as much time, effort, energy, and resources in learning this as I did in my medical specialty." Accepting both your strengths and your weaknesses will significantly reduce your stress. By accepting that you can seek support from those in your practice who *do* harbor these strengths, you will be more effective, and you will be squarely on the road to a new level of success.

··

Common Leadership Mistake
Thinking it is a leader's job to figure out the solutions, make the plans, and then present them to the staff

··

One area where this shift may manifest itself is in your reliance upon your office staff. As your thinking changes from "I should know this" to "Who in the office has the most knowledge and could lead the change in this area," your mindset may become more collaborative. Practice managers are one powerful resource that's often underused. You have the opportunity to empower your practice manager to make the greatest possible impact on your practice. As you search for ways to partner with your practice manager and identify what to hand off, we suggest that the two of you meet frequently. Start by each listing your strengths and then having a conversation about how to best use those strengths for the benefit of the practice. It may also be helpful to brainstorm about other external resources that would benefit the practice. Which tasks can you delegate that would be better accomplished by someone other than you? How can you follow and support rather than direct these efforts? What are the next steps in embracing and moving through the transformation the new system will require?

Next Steps

1. Be open to gathering suggestions from your entire team to discover new ways to move the practice to the next level. As detailed in chapter 4, have regular staff meetings in which you listen more than you talk. What you hear from others can provide a wealth of information for your practice.

   a. Maximize the value of your partnership with your practice manager, who can be one of the best sources of new ideas. Practice managers are also in a good position to observe and manage the implementation of ideas. This allows you to practice medicine and helps things move to the next level in your office. Teaming up with your practice manager could make a huge difference.

   b. Maximize the value of all managers in your practice. The front office lead, billing manager, nursing manager, and others who are responsible for areas of your practice (if it is large enough for this) are also excellent sources of new ideas and have the ability to oversee and monitor changes as they are implemented.

c. Maximize the value of your staff members. Most physicians have never been in those roles. Acknowledge that your staff knows and sees things every day from a very different perspective, and that they can provide unexpected insights and suggestions. We have found that most of the time, staff members really put their hearts into making a difference for the patients. If their actions are not consistent with this bigger commitment, it is often because they think they are not truly an important part of the team.

2. Plan how you can fully use each person's expertise, and then implement the plan. Embrace a philosophy that calls for everyone to work to the top of his or her license and for you to never do anything as a physician that someone else can do as well or better. When we do other people's jobs, it is disempowering for everyone involved. When we trust and support them to do their jobs, we empower them and further support the practice.

3. Regularly thank and acknowledge each person on your team. Go out of your way to sincerely compliment employees. Remind them their work really does matter!

Focusing on the Future

Our practices are changing dramatically. Once virtually free to operate as independent small businesses, medical practices are experiencing the consolidation seen in the airline, automotive, retail, and entertainment industries, among many others. The promise of independence is now changing to a demand for interrelation and interdependence in a world where each of us must choose, understand,

and play a specific role. We are still vital to the engine with a tremendous amount to offer, but we're only one part of the engine, and sometimes it's not the part we thought we would play.

This transformation will occur. It has to. As much as we might not want to face this head-on, we must recognize how many people are dying as a result of our healthcare system's mistakes and inefficiencies, as well as the economic drag medicine is placing on America. The importance of this transformation is clearly articulated in *The Healthcare Imperative* by the Institute of Medicine, where the effect of these costs on the federal government, local government, and private sector create the imperative for improvement.[3] The question is not whether we will change but when—and we each have to ask not whether our careers will be different but *what role* we want to play in the new system. Resistance is futile and impedes what's possible going forward.

....

Common Leadership Mistake
Wishing medicine could be the way it was in "the good old days"

....

We're in one of those moments when the only way out is through. Focusing on what's possible on the other side

---

3   Pierre L. Yong, Robert S. Saunders, and LeighAnne Olsen, editors, the National Academies Press, 2010, http://www.nap.edu, p. 69.

of these changes, and beginning to honor and embrace those possibilities, will dramatically increase the success of the transformation and the scope of our roles in the new system. Remember that each of us ultimately gets to choose our new roles and the quality of life we experience during the process and on the other side.

Although it is almost impossible to avoid initially feeling stressed and perhaps even somewhat victimized by these changes, once we successfully navigate them, we will experience a new level of empowerment. We will do this, in part, by effectively delegating the things that are not our strong suits and giving our time and energy to what we do best for the practice.

This is true no matter how you choose to participate— in an independent practice, in a large group, as an employee of a hospital, or in the administration, research, or business side of medicine. You have an opportunity to experience making *your* difference while also being part of an important team that is making a significant difference!

Practice

1. Continue to *listen for*, be a *learner*, and make your mission/vision statement a working document for your practice.

2. Meet with your practice manager and review your lists of strengths and weak spots. Discuss the tasks and areas of the business you can pass along to someone else in order to best serve your practice.

3. Set a timeline to delegate these areas in a realistic and effective manner.

4. Encourage your practice manager and your staff to read this book and apply the distinctions and concepts in your practice. Refer to this book when you are highlighting what's working and when you are addressing what's not working.

5. Enter weekly reminders on your calendar to acknowledge your staff members. Find opportunities to authentically acknowledge them for their work. (Some people think if this doesn't occur naturally, then it isn't sincere. We think entering it on your calendar and then following through shows you are serious about expressing your gratitude.)

Practice Manager Leadership

*Good leaders make people feel that they're at the very heart
of things, not at the periphery. Everyone feels that he or
she makes a difference to the success of the organization.
When that happens, people feel centered and that gives
their work meaning.*

Warren Bennis

> Take your unique influence with your physi-
> cians, team members, and patients to the
> next level and have your practice thrive.

This chapter is dedicated to speaking directly to you as
a practice manager. We hope you have read the first
eight chapters of this book and have begun to apply many
of the distinctions and recommendations to support your
practice. We would like to take the opportunity to give you
some additional information that pertains uniquely to your
leadership role in the practice.

As the practice manager, you have significant influence

in your practice. You're likely to be involved in every aspect of the practice—the business side as well as the medical side. Undoubtedly, you have significant knowledge of every moving part! You also have a direct role in supporting your staff members so they can both excel in their individual jobs and act as a unified team. There are many things you can do to make a positive impact in these areas. And there may be some things you are doing that unintentionally have the opposite effect.

Unify Your Team

Do you and your team experience being treated with respect? Could this be one of the key elements of effective leadership? When we have asked medical staff the question "What motivates you at work," we have typically received these answers: "receiving respect from the people I work with and for," "a sense that I really do make a difference," and "feeling appreciated." These answers are consistent with the global consulting firm Mercer's *What's Working* survey.[1]

---

1   Mercer, What's Working™ survey (October 27, 2011). "The global analysis reveals that nonfinancial factors play a prominent role in influencing employee motivation and engagement—a finding that could prove useful to employers facing budget constraints. Workers worldwide say that being treated with respect is the most important factor, followed by work/life balance, type of work, quality of coworkers, and quality of leadership."

. . . .

Common Leadership Mistake
Unintentionally dividing your team with your open-door policy

. . . .

Open-Door-Policy Pitfalls

First, we wholeheartedly support having an open-door policy. Your staff needs a go-to person for answers and support. It's crucial to demonstrate to your team members that you take your role in supporting them seriously and to continue to be actively involved in the day-to-day business of the practice. That said, let's examine the pitfalls we often see managers fall into with this policy. Your words can either unify your team or unintentionally divide it and reduce the experience of respect throughout.

Example:

David asks: "Hi, do you have a minute?"

Motioning to David to step into your office, you say, "Sure, come on in. What's up?"

David says, "Well, I thought you would want to know Linda has been texting, and she seems to waste a lot of time when you're not around. I'm always finishing up her stuff, and I just don't think it's fair."

You reassure David. "OK. Thanks for letting me know. I'll check into it."

You find Linda and say, "Linda, do you have a moment? Let's meet in my office."

Linda says, "Of course. What do you want to talk about?"

You say, "Well, it has been brought to my attention that you've been texting on your personal cell phone and falling behind on your work at times. Overall, I think you do a very good job. However, you know the drill, no personal cell phone use in the office unless it's an emergency."

Linda listens and then ends the conversation with the comment, "OK. I hope you know I'm not the only one."

Now you may think, "I did a pretty good job with that. David feels heard, plus I didn't brush anything under the rug. I addressed the situation with Linda, and I think she knows she can't get away with that anymore. So everything is good, right?" *We don't think so.* In this example, we would agree that you strengthened your relationship with David and had a nonconfrontational but straight conversation with Linda. However, David and Linda are not any closer. In fact, they are further apart. David now feels superior to Linda, and Linda feels betrayed by someone on the team and may suspect David.

We have heard practice managers say, "My staff act like kids sometimes. I thought we were all adults. Why can't everyone act like it?" First, we think it is important to remember that at times we have all become focused on finding fault with a situation or relationship and then acted like kids. And in the example above, tattling and defensive reactions were actually reinforced.

At this point you may be thinking, "Well, what can I do that would be better?" At your next staff meeting, you could tell everyone you've learned a new method that you think will support the entire team in going to the next level. Tell them as a group that from now on if they have any concerns or upsets with another person, you ask them to do the following:

1. *Listen for* each other and be *learners*. (Explain those two distinctions from chapter 1 if you haven't already.)

2. Remember that everyone on the team is committed to excellence and wants the practice to be successful—even if someone is currently taking actions that seem in conflict with that.

3. If you think another person on the team is doing something that doesn't work and needs to be addressed, have a conversation with that person in a respectful, professional, and constructive manner and look for solutions together. (Exception: if you think someone is doing something illegal, give that information to your PM.)

4. If you think another person on the team is doing something that doesn't work but really doesn't need to be addressed, sincerely let it go. Remind yourself that part of being an effective team is not dramatizing the small stuff. Don't stew about it, and don't gossip about it!

5. If a person on the team approaches you with concerns about something you're doing, be open and receptive. Keep in mind the bigger picture of having a cohesive team to best support our patients. Be a *learner* by being open-minded about the other person's ideas rather than reacting in a defensive manner. Respond as you would want another person to respond if you wanted to discuss

a concern. Remember that none of us are flawless. We reach the highest level of teamwork when we admit our mistakes and see situations from another person's point of view.

6. If the conversation is not constructive for both people, ask your practice manager to please mediate or guide the conversation to a successful conclusion.

After you make this announcement, reinforce it:

1. Go out of your way to find opportunities to acknowledge your staff when they sort out their concerns and differences in a productive manner.

2. If a staff member comes to you with a concern (and it's not a possible legal issue), ask, "Have you already talked with the other person?" If not, give a reminder that everyone is ultimately committed to the same thing in the practice and that it is vital to work together by sorting it out for themselves—although you're happy to mediate and support the conversation if they're not able to come to a resolution that works for both people.

3. When you do get involved in supporting a productive conversation between two staff members, never disempower them by saying, "I can't believe I had to get involved with this." Just know that over time, your staff will get stronger and stronger at having productive conversations when warranted and at letting go of the small stuff.

Another gift you can provide for your practice is being the role model for a gossip-free office. (Refer to chapter 4 for specifics on this topic. We have also included a section in chapter 10 to specifically support your employees in reducing gossip.) We encourage you to be very proactive, as you have significant influence in minimizing gossip on your team.

Feedback for Employees

Whether your staff is operating at an A+ level or not, we assert that giving employees regular day-to-day feedback, as well as formal feedback, sends the message and reinforces the fact that they are a very important part of the team.

....

Common Leadership Mistake
Viewing staff reviews as a chore instead of an opportunity for acknowledgment and growth

....

Think of a time when your manager procrastinated giving you a review. Maybe she would tell you she didn't think it was necessary or that it just didn't fit into her busy schedule. Even if you understood that her schedule was extremely busy and this made sense logically, you probably didn't feel that giving you feedback and highlighting your work was a priority for her. (Of course, an exception could be if you knew your job was on shaky ground. Then you might be relieved to have the review postponed.)

The annual review is the perfect opportunity to give your

staff acknowledgment as well as input on areas for improvement. Unfortunately, without a formal review, managers often put off talking about uncomfortable topics until the situation is urgent. By then, the employee has a significantly lower chance of correcting the problem and excelling.

Performance-Improvement Plans

....

Common Leadership Mistake

Disempowering your staff by not having members take the leadership role in their performance-improvement plans

....

Most often, a performance-improvement plan is put together by the manager, who then meets with the employee to notify him of what needs to happen. We think that's a bit like handing someone else a list of New Year's resolutions to accomplish. It is challenging enough to be successful when we create our own resolutions.

When we *listen for* our employees and remind ourselves that they are ultimately committed to excellence (even if their current actions don't reflect it), we can have conversations that give them input about what's not working so they can make the necessary corrections. Let them know that it is *their* career and therefore their responsibility to ensure their performance best serves the company—in this case, your medical practice. As a practice manager, you are there to provide input and support while employees take the leadership in their own job performance.

Example: You privately say to Linda: "Hi, let's meet in my office." After sitting down with the door closed, you say, "Linda, first I'd like to say that I know you're committed to the success of our practice and you bring a lot of skills and talents to your job that make a big difference here. I want to talk with you about a couple of areas that aren't working. First, you have been coming in late in the mornings. You've been late four times this month and three times the previous month. Second, I've overheard some of your phone conversations with patients, and you sound impatient or irritated with them."

Linda quickly replies, "Well first, about me being late, the traffic is crazy in the mornings. I can't control that."

You continue. "Of course, none of us can control the traffic; however we can plan accordingly. We would like for you to continue working here. A requirement for that is being on time and also shifting how you interact with patients on the phone, even when the situation is frustrating. As you know, we are committed to excellent patient care and to having our patients feel truly cared for. Do you have any questions about what needs to change?"

Linda says, "Well, I guess not."

You smile. "That's good. I hoped this would be clear for you. What is your plan to correct these two areas?"

Linda replies, "Well, I don't know."

You say, "Sure, this was our first meeting, and you didn't know we were going to discuss this today. Think it over for a couple of days, and write down your ideas for a plan of action. I will also make a list of ideas. Then let's meet again Thursday afternoon and finalize a plan. We really would love for this to work out and for you to continue to be on the team!"

We suggest that using this format will empower Linda. She is more likely to be responsible, rise to the occasion, and succeed. It's clear to her that it is her responsibility to shift her actions to best serve the practice, rather than your responsibility to somehow get her to shift. This is significantly different from what we often see in performance reviews. Without using this method, you are actually training your staff to be less self-sufficient.

When you have your second meeting with Linda, center the conversation on her ideas, and then add your ideas if appropriate. Schedule weekly meetings to review her success with the plan until it is stable.

Your staff is your most valuable resource for success. Regularly thank each of your team members and remind them of the difference they make!

Acknowledgment and Appreciation

Go out of your way to acknowledge your staff members both privately and publicly for what they do and the difference they make. Think about what will make each team member more likely to experience being appreciated. Also, highlight when they acknowledge each other.

Partnership with Physicians

Sharing the top leadership positions with the physician(s) in your practice can be tricky. The number one requirement is open communication between you and the physician. Every physician prefers to be involved with the day-to-day running of the practice in different ways. Have a conversation with your physician or physicians and find out what works for them and for the practice. Discuss not only the big picture but also the little details so you're clear on how to make things work. Decide who will talk with employees when something isn't working. Agree that you will each regularly acknowledge and compliment employees. Determine who will announce and reinforce new policies and changes. It is crucial that you are united in how the practice is run. Any inconsistency will be fuel for chaos and divisiveness on the team.

Ensuring Your Staff Know What to Do

As practice manager, another of your important roles is to ensure that your staff members have clear job descriptions and manuals and have been fully trained as well as cross-trained. To reach the highest level of efficiency in your practice, each employee needs to know what's expected of him or her as well as how to grow and really excel in that role. That's ongoing training. This ongoing training includes formal "customer service" training. Most people need specific training to be able to provide A+ customer service, especially in challenging situations. (One good resource for this type of training is www.CustomerServiceGroup.com.)

Part of this requires employees to speak up, and part of it is you observing, asking, and ensuring that they get the training they need. Consider this as a gift you're giving to your staff rather than another chore for you.

Having your staff cross-trained, especially in practices that are small and have few staff members, may seem impossible or unnecessary. Whenever possible, look for the opportunity and also ask your employees, "Are there any other parts of the practice or the business you would like to learn?" View this as a never-ending opportunity.

If a person decides to leave or a situation arises where you need to terminate an employee, having others who are able to step up and fill in the blanks until you hire a replacement allows the practice to run smoothly.

Your influence with your staff and the practice is significant. By using the suggestions in this chapter, you can ensure that you will have a positive influence with your physicians, your staff, and ultimately your patients.

Practice

1. Continue to *listen for,* be a *learner,* and make your mission/vision statement a working document for your practice.

2. Follow through with the suggestions for effective promises and requests, delegating to others and using an action grid.

3. Have regular staff meetings using suggestions from chapter 4 where you gain information and insights from your staff members as well as providing information for them.

4. During a staff meeting, share your new format for empowering and supporting team members in resolving their concerns by following the suggestions in this chapter.

5. Have regular meetings with the physicians in your practice so that you are in alignment and can provide unified leadership.

6. Provide an annual and midyear review for each of your staff members. Remind yourself that these reviews are an important way to highlight each person on the team, formally acknowledging their strengths as well as addressing their areas for improvement.

7. Read chapter 10 and reinforce those elements throughout your practice. Encourage your staff to read this book with a highlighted focus on chapter 10.

10

Employee Leadership

The key to successful leadership today is influence, not authority.

Kenneth Blanchard

> Learn how you can be a leader, no matter where you are on the organizational chart, and have an increased sense of fulfillment.

This chapter is dedicated to you as an employee of a medical practice. We hope you have read the earlier chapters of this book and have begun to apply many of the distinctions and recommendations to support your practice. We would like to take the opportunity to give you some additional information that pertains uniquely to your leadership role as an employee.

How you relate to everyone throughout the practice really does make a difference. Your interactions with your fellow staff members, your physicians, your practice manager, and most importantly, of course, the patients can add positive energy and make a positive difference. And whether you're aware of it or not, you could have the opposite effect.

....

Common Leadership Mistake
Thinking you have to be at the top of an organizational chart to be a leader

....

Often people think that if they're not in management positions and nobody on the organizational chart reports to them, then they must not be leaders. But no matter what your role in the practice—receptionist, medical assistant, nurse, technician, billing specialist, scheduler, etc.—you have the opportunity to be a leader. The question is, how do you provide leadership in your role, and will you choose to step up to that opportunity?

First, let's examine your role from the patient's point of view. You represent the doctors in your office. Many patients think doctors personally hire their medical staff, even though in most cases, that's not true. However, if an employee is doing a poor job and the patient doesn't feel well taken care of by that employee, it reflects on the doctor. And although the doctor may not have hired that employee, it is the doctor's right and responsibility to speak with the employee or the practice manager and require improvement.

Let's think about this from a different angle. You're having lunch in a restaurant, and you feel the server is rude and acts like he doesn't care. Unless this seems to be a rare situation, you will probably think the manager or owner of the restaurant doesn't care either. Otherwise, the situation with that employee would have been addressed, and the employee would have either improved or been fired.

Providing excellent customer service is a form of leadership for the practice. Two key elements of great customer service in any industry include: 1) Following through on what you say you are going to do, and 2) Being cheerful. It requires both. It cannot be just one or the other. Eye contact and a smile have a positive impact on your interactions.

For patients (and all humans), a smile (we mean a full smile with teeth showing) creates a unique connection. It alters the experience and helps the patient feel welcomed and cared for. Some staff members have told us they aren't in the mood and don't feel like smiling. Our advice? Do it anyway. It is that important for the patients.

The Power of a Smile

Recent neuroscience research has shown that when you smile (even a forced smile) it triggers your body to release serotonin,[1] reduces stress, and helps your heart.[2] So smiling is actually a benefit for *you* as well as the patient!

---

1   Adam Rinde, "When You're Smiling: Dopamine and Serotonin smiles with you," Sound Integrative Health Website, September 26, 2011, http://soundintegrative.com/blog/2011/09/26/when-your-smiling-dopamine-and-serotonin-smiles-with-you/. Sound Integrative Health Website, September 26, 2011.

2   Catharine Paddock, "Smiling Reduces Stress and Helps the Heart," August 1, 2012, http://www.medicalnewstoday.com/articles/248433.php. MNT.

The front desk is the first critical in-person experience for the patient. Consider it the opening act for the play called *Patient Visit*. Each subsequent interaction then either adds to or diminishes the experience for the patient.

When patients are welcomed in a cheerful and professional manner at the front desk and throughout their visit, they are more likely to believe the staff and the doctor actually care about them. Patients are then more likely to really listen to the doctor and follow the doctor's advice, which increases the likelihood of improved medical outcomes!

Your job is not to merely complete tasks throughout the day. Each person in a medical practice actually has an influence on medical outcomes for the patients. How billing questions or concerns are handled or how the scheduling of appointments is handled can influence how patients feel about the doctor and make it more or less likely that they'll follow through on their treatment plans.

Leadership Examples

Here are some additional examples of what it can look like when you're being a leader during a typical day in the office.

Example: You're working at the front desk when a previously seen patient named Mrs. Jones signs in. She doesn't look well and seems extra grumpy. Here are a few options for you:

1. Just keep working on your tasks and let it go. *(Might be appropriate.)*

2. Gossip with the other staff about how grumpy Mrs. Jones is today. *(Never appropriate.)*

3. Make a private phone call to give the practice manager or the medical assistant a heads-up. Report that from your perspective, Mrs. Jones is really out of sorts today and doesn't seem well. She may need more care than usual. Who knows, the medical assistant may have been on the phone with Mrs. Jones earlier that day and become aware that something critical might be developing. Your input may help to confirm those observations. *(Leadership!)*

Example: On a regular basis, you hear minor complaints from the patients in the waiting room about the wait time. Here are a few options for you:

1. You do nothing. You have concluded there's nothing you can do about it. Many front desk employees are disheartened by this issue. They feel bad that the patients have to wait, yet at the same time they certainly don't feel it's their job to do anything about it. *(Not appropriate unless your practice manager or physicians have specifically asked you not to get involved with this challenge.)*

2. You tell the patients you're sorry for the delay and ask whether you can get them something to drink—maybe coffee or a bottle of water. *(Excellent customer service.)*

3. At the next staff meeting, you ask for the opportunity to brainstorm solutions to reduce the

wait time for patients, and maybe even ask to be the project leader for that challenge. That doesn't mean you have to have all the answers. It means you would gather ideas and suggestions and take a direct leadership role in reducing wait times. It could actually be really exciting and make a difference for everybody involved. *(Leadership!)*

Example: You saw a problem with the air conditioner vent in the office and thought it could be important for the practice manager to know about it. Here are a few options for you:

1. You do nothing. The problem doesn't directly involve you, so why should you take it on? *(Doesn't make a positive difference and may have negative consequences if the practice manager is not informed.)*

2. You go to the practice manager and roll your eyes as you say, "You're not going to believe this, but we have another problem here!" You then proceed to dump the information in the practice manager's lap. *(Never appropriate.)*

3. You remind yourself that you are all one united team with a commitment to providing excellent medical care and customer service for your patients. You know your practice manager wants the office to operate at a level of excellence, as do you. You tell the practice manager, "I noticed the air conditioning vent in the waiting room is no longer functioning, and I wanted to let you know. Would you like for me to make a call, or is there

anything that I can do to help get it corrected?"
(Leadership!)

Welcoming New Employees

Have you ever looked back and realized you did not welcome and include a new employee until it was too late? Have you ever been on the receiving end of being tested or feeling like an outsider whom others expected to fail? If so, you know the cost of this surprisingly common behavior.

....

Common Leadership Mistake

Waiting until new employees have proved themselves before welcoming them to the team

....

Example: A new team member joins the practice. Here are a few options for you:

1. You say hi but nothing more than what is absolutely necessary to the new person until you think he's proved himself or you've decided you like him. *(Never appropriate.)*

2. You gossip with others about the new person and point out each time she makes a mistake or doesn't catch on quickly. *(Never appropriate.)*

3. You gossip with the new person about the others in the group who are not your favorites so that he will be on your side. *(Never appropriate.)*

4. You go out of your way to welcome her. You let her know you're available if she has any questions or concerns. You don't gossip with her about others. You speak highly of the physicians, staff, and patients. You invite her to have lunch with you or join some social activity with the group. *(Leadership!)*

When employees have a pattern of not truly welcoming and including new people, it leads to diminished team spirit and often a high turnover rate. We have seen the very people who have run off the new employees, in a sense, later grumbling about being overworked and understaffed. There is a very high cost to this pattern.

More about Gossip

Gossip is another area where you can make a positive impact and be a leader. This topic is covered in chapter 4 and also in chapter 9, but we want to touch on it again because the cost of gossip is significant.

. . . .

Common Leadership Mistake
Thinking gossip is just part of the norm

. . . .

Frequently we hear people say, "I don't gossip. I sure get an earful, but I'm not the one doing it." Let's clarify that it takes a speaking person and a listening person for gossip to occur. If I'm the speaking person and I'm talking to the wall about the person I'm irritated with, you may have concerns about my emotional and mental wellbeing, but no gossip is occurring. Another human has to listen for it to be gossip.

Human beings tend to have a strong desire to gossip and put people down, which is a bizarre way we try to feel better about ourselves or our circumstances. So refraining from saying something that puts another person down is a sign of self-esteem and self-respect.

How can you bow out of gossip? One idea is that when somebody starts to talk negatively about one of your teammates, physicians, or patients, you could say, "Gosh, we all do crazy things sometimes. Well, I've gotta get back to work." This is not about scolding the other person and saying, "You know we aren't supposed to gossip." In most cases, that's probably not going to be effective. Instead, one of our recommendations is to find humorous or light-hearted ways to just step back and bow out. You'll be doing yourself a huge favor. You'll feel better at the end of the day, and the overall harmony of the team will increase.

Empowerment for Everyone

Leadership includes empowerment up and down the organizational chart. We often think it's the job of our supervisors to empower us. That's true. It is part of their job. It is also part of our jobs because empowerment is a two-way street. How can you empower your supervisor? One thing you can do is ask. Select a time to have a private conversation, and say, "I'm really committed to giving my best here, and a key part of that is my relationship with you and supporting your role. Is there anything I could do differently that would be helpful for the practice or empowering for you?" After you ask, be open-minded and willing to listen.

Pay attention to the supervisor's point of view and share your own as well. Then acknowledge what the supervisor is doing that is already empowering for you, and make any suggestions you have about what would be more helpful or empowering for you. The supervisor doesn't have a crystal ball any more than you do, so speaking up and having open communication is one of the keys to having a harmonious staff that operates at a level of excellence.

Being a leader is a never-ending opportunity. You make a difference in your practice at every moment. Whether that difference is positive or negative is a choice. Bringing forth leadership is a never-ending opportunity!

Practice

1. Continue to *listen for*, be a *learner*, and make your mission/vision statement a working document for your practice.

2. Schedule a meeting with your practice manager to share your ideas about where you can be a leader in your role. Be open to input.

3. Each time you see something in the practice that you think needs to be addressed, present the information to the appropriate person in the most productive way possible.

Conclusion

The Value of Distinctions

It is our sincere wish that you have enjoyed and, more importantly, received real value from working through this book. We hope you will come back to it as a resource and share it again with your team whenever you are faced with a new or recurring challenge.

As you and your team integrate the distinctions and lessons from this book, you'll create an opportunity for a gradual transformation from an autocratic, doctor-oriented, highly controlled, and highly managed system to a more collaborative and empowered culture where every person on the team is expressing their authentic commitment to the practice's success. With this transformation, everyone on the team will be operating consistently with their commitment to great patient experiences and outstanding medical outcomes in a financially sustainable and successful practice.

This book shows a way to navigate the transformation process that really works. Unlike a short course in billing and collections, or a continuing medical-education course that evaluates participants with a fifty-question test at the end, mastery of this process takes patience and consistency. Each person reading the distinctions in this book will have his or her unique perspective and opinions. It's very likely some of the distinctions were aligned with your beliefs and were quickly understood and applied. Others may be more challenging and could take longer to absorb and put into practice.

Take, for example, the first distinction at the beginning of chapter 1. Trying to do everything yourself is one of the most pervasive patterns that most people can recognize and then transform into something far more workable. With the revelation that you don't have to do all that you're doing in your practice, you can start the inquiry into what you can successfully turn over to someone else and how to do that skillfully. Often, the first days or weeks are a period of contemplation and consideration of what could be turned over, how, and the possible implications. If you are at the top of the organizational chart, could this give you more time to do higher-level things or more time off to relax? Could it lead to making more money? Finally, you emerge with a list of items separated into three categories: those you can definitely turn over, possibly turn over, and not turn over. With time and experimentation, you accomplish the first list, begin work on the second, and even begin to consider a different approach to some of the things you really don't enjoy on the third list.

The importance of this becomes clear when you look at caring for patients in a primary care practice. Research has shown that in a primary care practice of 2,500 patients, a doctor who follows all of the national recommendations for the treatment of chronic disease will have to work 10.6

hours (*Ann Fam Med* 2005;3:209–214), for preventive care 7.4 hours (*Am J Public Health* 2003 Apr;93(4)635–41), for acute care 4.7 hours per day (J Fam Pract 1198;46:377–389), and non-patient care 2.1 hours per day (AAFP survey May 2005). That's 24.8 hours per day! This, by definition, requires team-based care with effective delegation. The question is not if, but what, will be turned over to the team. The exciting result is that once the team begins to perform on behalf of the doctor and confidence grows, more and more is turned over. Soon quality gaps in care, follow-up appointments, diabetes and weight loss teaching, and other protocol-related tasks are handed off.

Medical Edge was successful using this process with a result of an increase in compensation coupled with Bridges to Excellence recognition for many of the doctors over a five-year period of time—exactly what the Institute of Medicine and primary care initiatives are calling for in America.

This dynamic tension and gradual process of discovery and success energizes and transforms the workplace. As the emphasis shifts from trying to do it right and appearing to know it all to being part of a high-performance team that is continually open to learning and growing, resistance and struggle diminish. The focus moves from judging the past successes and failures with an eye on discipline and control to standing together in your shared commitment to the future and seeing what actions this calls you and the team to take. Team members can now articulate and discuss what didn't work well from a shared commitment, as opposed to playing the blame game to determine the appropriate consequence for the employee who "failed." Instead of criticizing each other, the team stands shoulder to shoulder, committed to a more functional and gratifying future. Rather than being a problem, failure to achieve the ideal result becomes a step toward identifying the best way to succeed.

A *knower* environment gradually transforms into a collective place of learning. An environment of reactivity shifts to one of inquiry and response as a team instead of independent and possibly uncoordinated action from individuals. Coworkers begin to feel supported and advocated for instead of judged and questioned. The focus has shifted to an exciting shared goal the team is working to achieve, not a series of tests to see if employees succeed or fail. The question being answered by the organization shifts from "Are these the right people?" to "What about this process works toward achieving our goals, and what does not?" The attitude of the leaders shifts to "What about our system supports our employees and our goals, and what does not?" Instead of questioning the employees' commitment, the culture honors their commitments, and the conversation shifts from "Why aren't you performing?" to "What conversations and possible system changes will support you in honoring your commitment to the team and the important work we're doing?" In this culture, people are more likely to take personal responsibility for their actions and are empowered to make appropriate changes.

This could perhaps lead to employees shifting to new roles or identifying new opportunities more aligned with their personal ambitions. There's also a chance that someone may come to understand that their job is not a good fit and decide to respectfully part ways. You will know you are successfully facilitating this process when you see improvement in the staff's satisfaction, the quality of patient care, the practice's finances, and the ease of operations. Many leaders have described being able to focus on the gradual improvement of the practice rather than on judging and enforcing the rules as a weight being lifted off their shoulders. The mission and vision of the practice is no longer directed; it is shared by all members of the team—from the person with the least risk and responsibility to the one with the greatest.

A metaphor that illustrates this shift is that of pulling a cart. A medical practice may occur to the doctor like a huge burden. They're yoked to the cart, doing unrelenting, backbreaking work. On the cart are the staff members and patients of the practice. The doctor considers herself responsible for providing the direction and energy to move things forward.

Through the adoption of the distinctions shared in this book, a shift begins to occur. The doctor recruits members of the staff and they begin to share the vision together. Staff members get off the cart and begin to help pull it. As more and more of them join the cause, the weight of the cart decreases, and it takes less energy from each individual to move the cart forward. In addition, now that there are more people pulling on the yoke, there is more energy to move forward, and the cart speeds up.

Over time, the patients on the back of the cart also begin to see the mission and, in their own ways, get off the cart and begin pulling it in the direction sought by the practice. As everyone does his or her part, the cart almost seems to move by itself. The fatigued, initially solitary leader feels relief and excitement as the vision becomes engrained and the practice begins to flourish in all respects.

This transformation is occurring in medical practices all

over the United States today. We sincerely hope it is occurring or has occurred for you. What medical practices do is vital to the wellbeing and health of individuals and of our country. Ironically, we believe the cure for the healthcare system calls for transformation at a whole-system level, and that it really begins within each practice, and more specifically within each individual in that practice.

We are confident that the distinctions in this book will support you wherever you are on this journey. Please consider us huge fans and your fellow travelers along this path. We look forward to hearing from you and possibly even working with you along the way.

You Are Here to Enrich the World

You are not here merely to make a living.
You are here in order to enable the world to live
more amply, with greater vision,
with a finer spirit of hope and achievement.
You are here to enrich the world,
and you impoverish yourself if you forget the errand.

Woodrow Wilson

Resources

Programs Custom Designed for Your Medical Group

"The Art of Medical Leadership" by Suzan Oran and Scott Conard, MD

"Excellent Customer Service" by Suzan Oran

Suggested Reading

Emerald, David. *The Power of TED* (*The Empowerment Dynamic™)*. Bainbridge Island: Polaris, 2006.

Emerald, David, and Scott Conard. *TED* (*The Empowerment Dynamic™) for Diabetes: A Heath Empowerment Story*. Bainbridge Island: Polaris, 2012.

Guiliana, John, Hal Ornstein, and Mark Terry. *31½ Essentials for Running Your Medical Practice*. Phoenix, MD: Greenbranch, 2011.

Kofman, Fred. *Conscious Business: How to Build Value Through Values*. Boulder: Sounds True, 2006.

Loehr, Jim, and Tony Schwartz. *The Power of Full Engagement: Managing Energy, Not Time, Is the Key to High Performance and Personal Renewal.* New York: The Free Press, 2003.

Zaffron, Steve, and Dave Logan. *The Three Laws of Performance: Rewriting the Future of Your Organization and Your Life.* San Francisco: Jossey-Bass, 2009.

Zander, Rosamund Stone, and Benjamin Zander. *The Art of Possibility: Transforming Professional and Personal Life.* New York: Penguin, 2002.

Action Grid

Area to Impact *What's Next* or *What's Not Working* or *Area of Concern*	Specific Action Item	By Whom	By When	Comments & Current Status *On Track* or *Ahead* or *Behind*	Actual Completion Date

Practice Name: _____

Action Grid Manager: _____

Date: _____

Suzan Oran

Suzan Oran is the founder of the consulting firm Suzan Oran and Associates. Ms. Oran provides executive coaching, workshops, and programs to enhance leadership and effective communication, increase productivity, and build cohesive teams. Her commitment is to help individuals and groups to contribute their utmost and operate at peak performance. She has worked with thousands of physicians and medical staff to support their success.

Since 1986, Ms. Oran's business has expanded across the United States through client referrals.

Ms. Oran served as the vice president of leadership development for Medical Edge Healthcare Group, where she designed and facilitated several programs, including a five-level Empowerment Program and Creating New Possibilities program for physicians, as well as Clinic Team-Building workshops and Excellent Customer Service workshops.

Prior to founding Suzan Oran and Associates, Ms. Oran was certified by and led communication and performance seminars for an international education firm.

Suzan Oran is a national speaker on topics such as Leadership That Shapes the Culture of Your Organization, Leading to Make a Positive Impact, and Listening—the Key to Excellent Customer Service, to name a few.

She presents four programs nationally on behalf of AbbVie, a biopharmaceutical company, to support and empower physicians and medical staff in fine-tuning their communication and relationship skills so that they can make the biggest difference possible with their patients.

Suzan also provides an interactive online Life Design program. Participants are empowered to take a leadership role in all aspects of their lives and use a unique process to intentionally and methodically design a life they love.

For more information visit www.SuzanOranandAssociates.com.

Scott Conard, MD

Dr. Conard works at the intersection of health-system effectiveness, organizational leadership, and individual wellbeing. In the twenty-six years he has practiced medicine, Dr. Conard has founded, developed, led, and sold five companies, including TienaHealth Medical Clinic, a proactive medical home; TienaHealth Research; Sleep Healers sleep labs; and Proactive Medical Management.

Dr. Conard has founded, developed, led, and sold five companies, including TienaHealth Medical Clinic, a proactive medical home; TienaHealth Research; Sleep Healers sleep labs; and Proactive Medical Management. During this time he was also an associate professor at UT Health Science Center in Dallas for twenty-one years and was a principle investigator in sixty-three clinical trials.

After merging TienaHealth with Medical Edge, a 510 provider and 1.3 million-patient, healthcare group, he served as chief medical and strategy officer. When Medical

Edge was sold to Texas Health Resources, he became the chief medical officer for Holmes & Murphy, an insurance brokerage firm, and then Compass Professional Health Services, a technology-enabled, price-transparent concierge, engagement, and population health company.

Currently he works to increase communication and collaboration between employers and medical providers to deliver outstanding medical care to employees with increased levels of quality, safety, and service while reducing overall program costs.

Working to share this vision through his books, programs, and consulting, Dr. Conard is committed to helping create a healthcare system that provides incentives for stakeholders to use technology and to empower people in order to add years to their lives and life to their years.

For more information visit www.scottconard.com.

Nicole Oran

Nicole Oran is a writer and journal-
ist. After receiving her bachelor's
degree in philosophy from Arizona
State University, Nicole went on
to complete her master's degree in
journalism with a focus in magazine
writing from the University of
Missouri. Her thesis project explored
interview techniques to be used to
increase communication and have an
open conversation when interviewing people in the enter-
tainment industry who have been directed or influenced by
a publicist.

She has done freelance writing and editing and
managed social media projects in several industries, such as
healthcare, executive coaching, and music. She is currently
a reporter for *MedCity News.*

Nicole also has also contributed to the Life Design
program as an accountability partner to participants
committed to powerfully moving their lives forward. In

addition, she has provided tutoring for students preparing for college entrance exams.

Nicole has a commitment to helping people create empowered lives through information, education, and support.

Connect with Us

Suzan Oran

For more information about having executive coaching, the Art of Medical Leadership program, or the Excellent Customer Service training custom designed for your practice, please contact Suzan Oran at:

E-mail: suzanoran@gmail.com

Website: www.SuzanOranandAssociates.com

Follow Me:

Scott Conard, MD

For more information about working with Dr. Conard, please contact him at:

E-mail: scott@scottconard.com

Website: www.scottconard.com or www.themdceo.com

Follow Me:

CPSIA information can be obtained at www.ICGtesting.com
Printed in the USA
LVOW08s1357260416

485377LV00002BA/86/P